WIDER WORLD 4

SECOND EDITION

CONTENTS

Unit 0	Good friends	2
Unit 1	You can do it!	6
Unit 2	Clean and green!	16
Unit 3	Looking good	26
Reading Time 1	Hanae Mori	36
Unit 4	Work hard, dream big!	38
Unit 5	To the stars and beyond	48
Unit 6	Good health	58
Reading Time 2	Nicholas Nickleby	68
Unit 7	Beyond words	70
Unit 8	Experience art	80
Unit 9	Party time!	90
Reading Time 3	The Garden Party	100
Exam Time 1	Units 1-3	102
Exam Time 2	Units 1-6	105
Exam Time 3	Units 1-9	108
Self-checks answer key		111

Good friends

0

VOCABULARY
Relationships | School | Using everyday technology | Holidays and travel | Transport | Hobbies and free time activities

GRAMMAR
Present Simple | Adverbs of frequency | Wh- questions | Comparatives and superlatives | Present Continuous | Past Simple | Present Perfect | For and since

0.1
Relationships | Present Simple | Adverbs of frequency | Wh- questions | School | Comparatives and superlatives

---

GRAMMAR A — Present Simple, adverbs of frequency, wh- questions

Present Simple
I live in London.
I don't like doing sports.
Do you live near your cousins? Yes, I do./No, I don't.
Does she go to your school? Yes, she does./No, she doesn't.
She likes acting.
She doesn't do First Aid classes.

Adverbs of frequency
always, never, usually, often, rarely, sometimes

Wh- questions
Where do you live?
When do you see friends?
Who do you hang out with?
Which school do you go to?
Why do you like your home?
What sports do you play?
How often do you visit your relatives?

GRAMMAR B — Comparatives and superlatives

Comparatives
The new library is bigger than the old one.
Art is more interesting than Science.
Practical exams are better/worse than written exams.

Superlatives
The classrooms have the latest technology.
The first day back at school is the most difficult.
It's the best/worst school in the area.

---

1 Write the correct word for each definition.
1. someone who studies with you in the same class: c l a s s m a t e
2. a member of your family: r_ _ _ _ _ _ _
3. your mother's mother: g_ _ _ _ _ _ _ _ _ _ _
4. your father's or mother's sister: a_ _ _ _
5. someone who lives near you: n_ _ _ _ _ _ _ _
6. a girl with only one parent the same as yours: h_ _ _ _ -s_ _ _ _ _

---

2 Complete the dialogue with the Present Simple form of the verbs in brackets.

Kay: Hi, I'm Kay. ¹<u>Do you go</u> (you/go) to this school?
Jan: Yes, I do, but it's my first day here.
Kay: Don't worry! I ² _____ (love) studying here. Everyone is really friendly. My older sister ³ _____ (study) here too, but she ⁴ _____ (not always/walk) to school with me.
Jan: I see. So, where ⁵ _____ (you/live)? Is it near here?
Kay: Yes, it is. I ⁶ _____ (usually/walk) to school, but I ⁷ _____ (sometimes/ride) my bike.
Jan: Oh, that's nice. Who ⁸ _____ (you/hang out) with here?
Kay: Those are my friends. They ⁹ _____ (always/arrive) early. Come on. I'll introduce you.
Jan: Great, thanks!

3 Choose the correct option.
1. (Physics)/ History is my favourite subject at school. I like all the science subjects.
2. Do you think we can work on our practical exam / project together?
3. We need to revise / learn for the test tomorrow.
4. It's lunchtime! Let's go to the canteen / library.
5. What did you revise / learn at school today?

4 Complete the sentences with the comparative or superlative form of the adjectives in brackets.
1. Our school is <u>the best</u> (good) school in the area.
2. I think Maths is _____ (difficult) subject.
3. Our new classroom is _____ (big) than the old one.
4. The new computer room has _____ (late) technology.
5. My new school is _____ (exciting) than my old school.

0.2 Present Continuous | Using everyday technology

GRAMMAR Present Continuous

He's studying Turkish this year.
I'm not learning very fast.
Are you exploring the city? Yes, I am./No, I'm not.

Time expressions
at the moment, now, right now, this month, this year, today

1 Choose the correct option.

1. *Are* / *Do* you reading anything good at the moment?
   — No, *I'm not* / *I don't*. I'm too busy with homework.

2. What are you doing *exactly* / *right* now? Are you busy?
   — No, *I not* / *I'm not* doing anything important.

3. What are you *studying* / *study* in History class this year?
   — *We* / *We're* learning about the American Civil War.

4. *Are* / *Do* you having a good time?
   — Yes, fantastic! I'm *talk* / *talking* to lots of interesting people.

2 Complete the sentences with the Present Continuous form of the verbs below.

| call | enjoy | ~~have~~ | not look forward to |
| study | watch | | |

1. I *'m having* lunch right now. Can I call you back?
2. What _____ (Jo and Ian) on the TV? It looks interesting.
3. Gary _____ English class because he hasn't done his homework.
4. We _____ the Romans in History this month.
5. Where _____ (you) from? It sounds noisy.
6. _____ (your sister) her new school?

3 **WORD FRIENDS** Label the pictures with a verb from box A and a word/phrase from box B.

A

| chat | download | ~~make~~ | post | text | write |

B

| an app | a blog | ~~a video~~ | on social media |
| someone | with people | | |

1. *make a video*
2. _____ 
3. _____ 
4. _____ 
5. _____ 
6. _____ 

4 Choose the correct option.

1. I'd like to *write* / *upload* a blog, but I don't have enough time.
2. I prefer *messaging* / *writing* people to phoning them.
3. How often do you *watch* / *go* online to check your email?
4. For homework, we have to *write* / *film* a video of ourselves speaking English.
5. How can I *download* / *watch* songs to listen to on my phone?
6. When you take pictures, do you *download* / *upload* them to a website or just keep them for yourself?

3 Unit 0

0.3 Holidays and travel | Past Simple | Transport

GRAMMAR Past Simple

They *stayed* in a hotel. (regular verb)
We *had* a great holiday. (irregular verb)
They *didn't stay* in a campsite.
Did you *hire* a car?   Yes, I *did*./No, I *didn't*.
When did he *come* here?

Time expressions
earlier this morning, in 2020, last summer, over a year ago, the day before yesterday, yesterday, when she was …

1 Mark the photos T (means of transport), H (type of holiday), A (accommodation) or Ac (activity). Then complete the words.

1 [H] c<u>ity</u> b<u>reak</u>

2 [ ] f_____

3 [ ] h_____

4 [ ] c_____

5 [ ] c_____

2 Write the Past Simple form of the verbs.

1 come   *came*   6 spend _____
2 leave _____   7 stay   _____
3 hire   _____   8 meet   _____
4 go   _____   9 travel _____
5 have   _____   10 make   _____

3 Complete the text with the Past Simple form of the verbs in brackets.

My last holiday

Last summer we ¹*went* (go) on holiday to the south of France. We ² _____ (stay) on a campsite near the beach and we ³ _____ (not do) much, just sunbathing. I ⁴ _____ (read) a lot of books and it ⁵ _____ (be) very relaxing. I also ⁶ _____ (make) a lot of friends my age, and in the day, we ⁷ _____ (hang out) together around the swimming pool. One day we ⁸ _____ (not meet) at the swimming pool. Instead, we went to a local art market and ⁹ _____ (not come) home until the evening. The next morning, my parents asked me, 'Where ¹⁰ _____ (you/go) yesterday?' When I ¹¹ _____ (tell) them, they ¹² _____ (not be) happy. So, I ¹³ _____ (draw) them a nice picture of the town where we were. They really liked it and they weren't angry with me anymore.

4 **WORD FRIENDS** Match the sentence halves.

1 [b] At what age can you drive
2 [ ] I would love to fly
3 [ ] Hurry up! We need to catch
4 [ ] My uncle taught me how to sail
5 [ ] Can we ride
6 [ ] Let's take

a the bus in ten minutes!
b ~~a car in your country?~~
c a bus – it's cheaper than the train.
d a horse on the beach today?
e a helicopter one day.
f a yacht on holiday last year.

Unit 0 4

0.4 Hobbies and free time activities | Present Perfect | For and since

GRAMMAR — Present Perfect

Affirmative
He *has* (just/already) *directed* a film.
They *have moved* to England.

Negative
I *haven't* (ever)/I *have* never *lived* in the US.
He *hasn't taken* part in a marathon (yet).

Questions
Have you (ever) *visited* the US?   Yes, I *have*./No, I *haven't*.
Has she (ever) *run* a 5K race?   Yes, she *has*./No, she *hasn't*.

For and since
They've lived in England *for* a year. (a period of time)
She's been here *since* April. (a point in time)

1 **WORD FRIENDS** Complete the sentences with the correct form of the verbs below.

direct   discover   hang out   ~~run~~   take (x3)

1 I *ran* a race at sports day today, but I didn't win.
2 Excuse me, could you _____ a photo of us in front of that building?
3 My dad _____ part in the London Marathon last year.
4 What I love about this city is that you can always _____ new places you didn't know existed.
5 Jo's mum _____ a film when she was at university.
6 I want to _____ up a new hobby, but I'm not sure what. Any ideas?
7 I'm going to _____ with my friends all weekend.

2 Complete the sentences with *for* or *since*.

1 I've known Hannah *since* we were three years old.
2 We've been at this school _____ six months.
3 Carla hasn't read a book _____ last February.
4 I've had my cat _____ nearly ten years.
5 I haven't eaten anything _____ lunchtime.
6 They haven't watched a film at the cinema _____ ages.

3 Use the prompts to make sentences in the Present Perfect.

1 you / ever / study / abroad / ?
   Have you ever studied abroad?
2 Fiona / not do / her homework / yet
   _____
3 my parents / already / meet / my new friend from school
   _____
4 Mark / feed / the cat / yet / ?
   _____
5 we / not go / camping / for two years
   _____
6 the programme / just / start
   _____

4 Complete the second sentence with the word in bold so that it means the same as the first one. Use no more than three words.

1 We moved here in 2021 and we live here now. **HAVE**
   We *have lived here* since 2021.
2 I haven't been to China at any time in my life. **NEVER**
   I _____ to China.
3 We are still waiting for the class to start. **YET**
   The class has _____.
4 I liked comedies when I was younger and I still like them now. **ALWAYS**
   I _____ comedies.
5 James met Fiona six months ago and they are friends now. **FOR**
   James has known Fiona _____.
6 Was there any time in your life when you had a pet cat? **EVER**
   Have _____ a pet cat?
7 I last saw my whole family at my birthday party. **NOT**
   I _____ my whole family since my birthday party.

You can do it!

VOCABULARY
Adjectives of emotion | Verbs of success and failure | Phrasal verbs for achieving goals | Phrases for achieving goals | Immigration | Personality adjectives

GRAMMAR
Present tenses | Past Simple, Past Continuous and Present Perfect

1.1 Vocabulary
Success, failure and goals

1 ● Match the adjectives below with pictures A–F. There are two extra adjectives.

| calm | cheerful | ~~confused~~ | delighted | exhausted |
| stressed | surprised | upset | | |

A _confused_

B _____

C _____

D _____

E _____

F _____

2 ●● How would you feel in each situation? Complete the adjectives of emotion.

1 You think you do well in an exam, but then you get a bad mark. c o n f u s e d
2 You've just received the smartphone you wanted as a present. d__ __ __ g __ t __ __
3 You're lying on the beach on holiday. c__l__
4 You're just about to do an important exam. a__ __ i __ __ __ __
5 You have lots of homework to do and don't have much time. s__ __ __ s __ __ d
6 Your friend visits you and you weren't expecting it. s__ __ p __ __ s __ __
7 You work hard on a project and get a good mark for it. p__ __ __ s __ __
8 You've had a really long day at school. e__ h __ __ __ __ t __ __

3 ●● Choose the correct answer.

1 I feel ___ after I have a nap.
   (a) calm   b stressed   c anxious
2 Anna was ___ with herself when she failed the exam.
   a pleased   b calm   c disappointed
3 Gwen's such a ___ person. She always has a smile on her face.
   a cheerful   b confused   c surprised
4 After spending weeks on their project, Ava and Noah were ___ when they finished.
   a anxious   b pleased   c upset
5 People gave me lots of different advice about the exam, which made me feel ___.
   a delighted   b cheerful   c confused
6 James was really ___ when he had a big argument with his parents.
   a calm   b upset   c exhausted

4 ● **WORD FRIENDS** Choose the correct option.
1 try / (take) it easy
2 make / do progress
3 make / do your best
4 put / get things done
5 give / get something a go
6 make / do decisions
7 make / do mistakes
8 make / take something seriously
9 make / do the most of something
10 take / get something right/wrong

5 ●● Complete the sentences with the words below.

~~achieve~~	aims	go	improve	made	making
managed	mistakes	reach	succeed	take (x2)	

1 Nick won't *achieve* his goals if he doesn't _____ them seriously.

2 Sometimes it's good to make _____ because you can learn from them and _____.

3 You might not always _____ when you try something new, but it's important to give it a _____.

4 Gillian has _____ a lot of progress at school this year. I'm amazed at what she's _____ to do.

5 I'm terrible at _____ decisions. That's why I never _____ my targets!

6 Our team always _____ to win. That's why we never _____ it easy in training!

6 ● Match the sentence halves.
1 [b] You can't put your homework
2 [ ] Come on, you can do this. Don't give
3 [ ] Carla's had a great year in Maths. I hope she keeps
4 [ ] If you've got something big to do, try breaking it
5 [ ] That's enough TV for now – it's time to get
6 [ ] That player's brilliant. I just can't work

a on working like this next year.
b ~~off any longer.~~
c on with your cleaning.
d down into smaller tasks.
e up!
f out how he does it.

7 ●●● Choose the correct option.

My thirty-day vegan challenge

This month I'm getting out of my comfort zone! How? I'm ¹(aiming) / achieving / failing to stop eating meat and animal products for thirty days. I'm not a vegan. In fact, I really like meat, but recently I read about the way many animals are treated and it made me feel really ²delighted / upset / exhausted. I decided to ³make / get / take this seriously and ⁴give / get / make a vegan diet a go.

I'm a bit ⁵cheerful / anxious / calm about eating plant-based products all the time and I'm worried about getting hungry, but I really don't want to ⁶fail / succeed / reach, so I'm going to ⁷make / get / do my best.

I've just finished my first day and I had lots of grains and nuts with soy milk for breakfast. I've made the ⁸progress / mistake / decision to have a cooked lunch every day now. In the evening, I had a salad with chickpeas and nuts. The good news is that I think I've ⁹got / taken / given things right with what to eat. A positive first day, I think, so I feel ¹⁰stressed / pleased / exhausted with myself!

Come back tomorrow to read about day 2!

I can talk about facing challenges, motivation and emotions.

On the Portal
Extra Practice Activities: Lesson 1.1

7 Unit 1

1.2 Grammar
Present tenses

GRAMMAR — Present tenses

Present Simple
I always press 'Snooze' when my alarm goes off. (routine)
I don't find it easy to get up. (permanent situation)

Present Continuous
Lots of people are listening to this podcast right now. (present action)
This term I'm trying to change my routine. (temporary situation)
He's making progress this term. (changing situation)

State verbs
belong, know, prefer, etc.
I know you're always at school early. NOT I'm knowing

State and dynamic verbs
I think I need help! (state verb: opinion)
What are you thinking about? (dynamic verb: mental process)

1 ● Match the verbs in bold in sentences 1–5 with functions a–e.
1 c I **know** the answer.
2 ☐ Chris **is doing** his homework.
3 ☐ Sara **works** in a hospital.
4 ☐ I'm **working** at a restaurant for the summer.
5 ☐ I **get up** at 7 a.m. on weekdays.

a a temporary situation
b a present action
c ~~a state verb~~
d a routine
e a permanent situation

2 ●● Choose the correct option.
1 My aunt and uncle (have) / are having two children. They go / 're going to the same school.
2 I don't agree / 'm not agreeing with the government's new education policy. What do you think / are you thinking?
3 I don't watch / 'm not watching TV at the moment. I do / 'm doing my homework.
4 We stay / 're staying in a different hotel this year because the place where we usually stay / 're usually staying is closed for the summer.
5 I never ask / 'm never asking Phil for the answer. He doesn't know / isn't knowing.

3 ●● Complete the sentences with the Present Simple or Present Continuous form of two of the verbs in brackets.
1 I _hear_ you_'re learning_ to play the drums. Is that true? (hear/learn/prefer)
2 I usually _____ for the school bus, but this morning I _____ a lift from my dad. (get/take/wait)
3 How much _____ your rucksack _____? It _____ really heavy. (weigh/look)
4 Quick, the film _____! You _____ the best part! (finish/miss/start)
5 I _____ my football coach because she always _____ me to do my best. (encourage/give/like)

4 ●●● Complete the email with the Present Simple or Present Continuous form of the verbs below.

close   do   enjoy   have (x2)   love   ~~not know~~
not work   practise   sell   stay   want

✉

Hey, Ben!

How are things?

I ¹_don't know_ if you know, but I've got a summer job in Munich. I ²_____ with my cousins who live here. It's great and I ³_____ myself a lot. I'm working in a small shop which ⁴_____ designer clothes and the other people who work in the shop are really nice. We always ⁵_____ lots of fun in the day. In the evening, when the shop ⁶_____, we usually all ⁷_____ dinner together somewhere. I ⁸_____ Munich! It's a really interesting city and I ⁹_____ my German too!

What ¹⁰_____ (you) this summer? ¹¹_____ (you) to come and visit me in Munich? It would be great to see you again and there's lots of space at my cousins' house, so you can stay with us. I ¹²_____ at weekends, so we could spend some time together. Let me know!

Harry

Unit 1 **8** I can use different tenses to talk about the present.

On the Portal
Extra Practice Activities: Lesson 1.2

1.3 Reading and Vocabulary
A new life abroad

1 Match the words below with the definitions.

> ~~new arrival~~ explore face a challenge immigrant
> migrant miss population stereotype support
> translate

1 someone who comes to a place: *new arrival*
2 the number of people living in a particular area or country: _____
3 someone who enters a country to live there: _____
4 have to deal with a difficult situation: _____
5 change written or spoken words into another language: _____
6 travel around an area to find out more about it: _____
7 someone who moves to another area or country, especially in order to find work: _____
8 a belief about what a group of people or things are like, often not true: _____
9 feel sad because you don't have or can't do something you had or did before: _____
10 encouragement or help from other people: _____

2 Read the article quickly and answer the question.
Which countries are mentioned?
_____

3 Read the article again and complete the sentences. Write no more than three words in each gap.

1 Connor came to Andalusia because he wanted to travel far *away from home*.
2 In Spain, you can eat tapas in a _____.
3 People speak about _____ dialects of Spanish in Mexico.
4 In China, Connor worked as an _____.
5 For him, the best thing in China was the _____.
6 He disagrees when people say that Americans always _____.

I can understand an article about immigrants and the problems they face.

CONNOR'S WORLD

Travelling can be a challenge. We asked travel blogger Connor Jones about his experiences.

At the moment Connor is in Andalusia, a region in the south of Spain. It's famous for its beaches, festivals, flamenco and for its delicious tapas. A tapa is a snack that you can get in a bar or restaurant. Connor has come here because he wanted to travel far away from home. Another reason was to practise the Spanish he learned in Mexico last year, but the Spanish here is different from the Spanish in Mexico, as many arrivals from the USA quickly learn.

In Mexico, although Spanish is widely spoken, it varies a lot. There are about 350 local dialects. So understanding everything as he travels around Spain is one of the challenges he faces. However, people are very friendly to foreigners, so he gets a lot of support. The cost of living is also very cheap – he gets a meal in an average restaurant for around five euros.

You may wonder where he gets the money for his travels. The answer is easy: he works as an English teacher. 'My first teaching job was in China and it was a dream come true!' he says. He went to Shanghai and he thought everybody knew some English. But he was wrong and had to learn Chinese really fast. It's a difficult language and the Chinese letters, called characters, are quite complicated. And like in Mexico, there are different languages and dialects. His favourite thing about China, though, was the transport. Public transport in the main cities is good. It's also easy to explore different parts of the country and discover new places.

It's interesting for Connor to find out what people around the world think of Americans. One thing he doesn't like is the stereotypes about American people, mainly that they all eat junk food, which just isn't true. Connor always tries the local food when he visits a place. He thinks this is important.

On the Portal
Extra Practice Activities: Lesson 1.3

1.4 Grammar
Past Simple, Past Continuous and Present Perfect

GRAMMAR — Past Simple, Past Continuous and Present Perfect

Past Simple
In 2014 she *reached* the top of Mount Everest. (finished action)
The temperature often *fell* as low as −35°C. (repeated action)

Past Continuous
It *was raining* on Sunday afternoon. (background description)
At three o'clock we *were watching* a film about Poorna Malavath. (action in progress)

Past Simple and Past Continuous
The teacher *was speaking* when some officials *came* into the classroom. (a longer action interrupted by a shorter one)

Present Perfect
She *has become* famous. (result in the present)
She *has climbed* Mount Aconcagua. (experience)

Present Perfect and Past Simple
Poorna *has climbed* many mountains. She *climbed* Mount Everest in 2014.

1 ● Choose the correct option. Then mark the sentences PS (Past Simple), PC (Past Continuous) or PP (Present Perfect).
1. Roshan *has had* / *was having* dinner with his family at 8 p.m. last night. **PC**
2. I *got up* / *was getting up* early every day last week. ____
3. *Did you ever have* / *Have you ever had* an unusual pet? ____
4. When we left the cinema, it *rained* / *was raining*, so we took the bus home. ____
5. My older brother *became* / *has become* a father in 2020. ____

2 ●● Use the prompts to make sentences in the Past Simple, Past Continuous or Present Perfect.
1. I / get / home / half an hour ago
   I got home half an hour ago.
2. my sister / start / school / last year
   _____
3. you / ever / play / baseball / ?
   _____
4. we / talk / about Maisie / when / she / walk / in
   _____
5. it / snow / when / I / wake up / this morning
   _____
6. when / I / be / little, / I / not like / broccoli
   _____

3 ●●● Complete the second sentence with the word in bold so that it means the same as the first one. Use no more than four words.
1. I first met Tom when I was five.
   I *have known Tom since* I was five. **KNOWN**
2. Jay started watching a film at 7.30 p.m. and finished at 9 p.m.
   Jay _____ at 8 p.m. **WAS**
3. Fiona isn't here now because she went to school earlier.
   Fiona _____ to school. **GONE**
4. I started having a shower, but then the water went cold.
   I _____ when the water went cold. **HAVING**
5. She didn't eat all morning and she didn't eat this afternoon.
   She _____ all day. **EATEN**

4 ●●● Complete the dialogue with the Past Simple, Past Continuous or Present Perfect form of the verbs below.

be ~~climb~~ do fall read recover stay visit (x2) walk

A: Hey, Nikki, how was your holiday?
B: Great, thanks! I ¹*climbed* a really big mountain!
A: Wow, really?
B: Yes, it was amazing – the most exciting thing I ² _____ ever _____, really.
A: I ³ _____ never _____ climbing, but I'd love to try it. So, where did you go?
B: Well, while I ⁴ _____ with my cousin in Scotland, we decided to climb Ben Nevis.
A: Yes, I ⁵ _____ all about it – although I ⁶ _____ never actually _____ Scotland. Wow! So, how was it?
B: Amazing, but while we ⁷ _____ up, one girl ⁸ _____ and hurt her leg.
A: Oh no! What happened next?
B: Well, a helicopter came and took her to hospital. She ⁹ _____ since then and she's fine now. And how was your holiday?
A: Not as exciting as yours – I just ¹⁰ _____ my gran in the country.

I can use different tenses to talk about past events and experiences.

On the Portal
Extra Practice Activities: Lesson 1.4

1.5 Listening and Vocabulary
Projection mapping

1 Use the clues to complete the crossword with adjectives of personality.

[Crossword grid with the following filled letters: 1 down starts with "a-c-t-i-v-e"; 4 across starts with "g"; 5 across starts with "r-e"; 6 down starts with "p"; 8 across starts with "c"; 7 down starts with "g"; 9 down starts with "s"; 10 across starts with "c"]

Across
4 My grandfather was a very _____, caring man. He wouldn't hurt a fly!
5 You can trust Sandy. She's very _____.
8 My brother is so _____. He always has to win at everything.
9 My sister is the _____ one in our family. She always makes the right decisions.
10 I'm _____ to know where you got those shoes from.

Down
1 I try to be as *active* as possible, so I play several sports.
2 I'd love to do a job where I can be _____, thinking of new ideas every day.
3 I wish I was more _____. My things are always in a mess and I can never find anything!
6 I know you're hungry, but you need to be _____. Dinner won't be ready for another hour.
7 It was very _____ of you to give me your book, thank you.

2 🔊 1.1 Listen to an interview with Miles Baker, a projection mapping artist. Put topics a–d in the order he talks about them.
a ☐ the different uses of projection mapping
b ☐ the history of projection mapping
c ☐ why he enjoys his work
d ☐ an explanation of what projection mapping is

3 🔊 1.1 Listen again and complete the notes.

> **Projection mapping**
> - projecting an ¹*image* onto something, e.g. the ² _____ of a building or inside a building, like a ³ _____
> - often includes sound and, together with the images, tells a ⁴ _____
> - not a modern art form; first started in the ⁵ _____
> - one of the first projection mapping displays was in Disneyland in ⁶ _____
> - uses: art, advertising, ⁷ _____, restaurants, smart appliances in modern homes, e.g. ⁸ _____

I can understand a conversation about projection mapping.

On the Portal
Extra Practice Activities: Lesson 1.5

1.6 Speaking
Asking for and offering help

1 🔊 **1.2** Listen and repeat the phrases.

SPEAKING Asking for and offering help

Asking for help
Can/Could you help me?
Would you mind helping me?
Can/Could you give me a hand (with this box)?

Replying
Of course.   Sure!
Sorry, I can't.   Of course not.
I'll be with you in a minute.

Offering help
Do you need any help/anything else?
Can I get you anything?
Can/May I help you?
Do you need/Can I give you a hand?
What can I do for you?

Replying
That would be great, thanks.
That's really nice of you, thanks.
Thanks for helping/your help.
No, I'm fine, but thanks anyway.

2 Order the words to make questions.
1. me / a hand / can / give / you / ?
   Can you give me a hand?
2. else / need / you / do / anything / ?
   _____
3. you / get / can / anything / I / ?
   _____
4. need / a hand / you / do / ?
   _____
5. me / could / help / you / ?
   _____
6. a hand / can / you / give / I / ?
   _____
7. help / may / you / I / ?
   _____
8. you / can / for / what / I / do / ?
   _____
9. with / give / you / my / me / a hand / could / homework / ?
   _____
10. you / me / would / helping / mind / ?
    _____

3 Match questions 1–7 with responses a–g.
1. [b] Can I get you anything to drink?
2. [ ] This exercise is too difficult. Can you help me?
3. [ ] May I help you? You look lost.
4. [ ] You seem stressed. Can I give you a hand?
5. [ ] Can you give me a hand with these bags?
6. [ ] Would you mind helping me? I'm looking for the staff room.
7. [ ] Here are the books you ordered. Do you need anything else?

a That would be great, thanks. I just don't understand this Maths problem.
b ~~No, thanks. I'm fine.~~
c That's really nice of you, thanks. I'm looking for the station.
d No, these are all I need. Thanks for your help.
e Of course not! I'll show you.
f Sure! I'll be with you in a minute.
g Of course! Let me carry these two for you.

4 🔊 **1.3** Complete the dialogue with one word in each gap. Then listen and check.

Jess: Steph, could you give me a ¹*hand* with something?
Steph: ²_____! I'll be with you in a ³_____. Sorry about that. What can I help you with?
Jess: I'm having problems with my Maths homework – it's really difficult. Would you ⁴_____ helping me?
Steph: Oh sorry, Jess. I'm really bad at Maths.
Matt: Can I ⁵_____ you a hand, Jess? Maths is my best subject.
Jess: That's really ⁶_____ of you, Matt, thanks. Could you ⁷_____ me with number three, here?
Matt: Of course! Let me look. Oh, it's simple – see? You just need to add these two numbers together and divide the total by this number.
Jess: Ah, I see! Thanks for ⁸_____!
Matt: No problem. Do you need anything ⁹_____?
Jess: No, I'm ¹⁰_____, thanks.

Unit 1 12 I can ask for and offer help.

On the Portal
Extra Practice Activities: Lesson 1.6

1.7 Writing

A blog post describing a personal challenge

1 Match the verbs below with the definitions.

cry   scream   shake   shiver   shout   sweat

1 produce tears from your eyes, usually because you're unhappy or hurt: *cry*
2 produce liquid on the surface of your skin because you're hot or nervous: _____
3 when part, or all, of your body moves quickly because you're afraid or cold: _____, _____
4 make a loud, high noise because you're afraid or hurt: _____
5 say something very loudly: _____

2 Complete Antje's description of a personal challenge with phrases a–f.

a But when I heard about a new talent show at my school
b I normally love
c The experience has made me
d When I arrived at
e The problem is
f At the beginning, it was difficult

My first performance
by Antje Fischer

¹*b* singing and I do it whenever I can at home – usually in the shower! ² ___, I've always hated singing in public or even in front of my closest friends. The thought of it makes me feel really anxious. ³ ___, I decided to give it a go.

⁴ ___ the contest, I walked onto the stage and I was terrified. My hands were shaking and I could hardly hold the microphone. When the music started, I was shivering all over, but I began to sing the first few words. ⁵ ___, but gradually, I started to calm down and sing better. By the end, I actually wanted to scream with joy – I loved it!

I didn't win the contest, but people said I sang well. ⁶ ___ more confident about my singing – I'm even thinking about joining a band!

3 Match the sentence halves.

1 [c] I first realised I had a problem
2 [ ] When I heard about the competition,
3 [ ] That day, I learned
4 [ ] Now I'm not afraid

a of heights any more.
b something important about myself.
c when I went climbing with a friend.
d I decided to give it a go.

4 Complete Toby's notes about his personal challenge with phrases a–d.

a always been afraid of water
b feel more confident on the water now
c realised when I travelled by ferry as a child
d nervous at first, shivering and sweating

Sailing a boat
Reason for the challenge
• ¹*always been afraid of water*
• ² _____
• uncle has a boat, invited us to go sailing
Description of the challenge
• ³ _____
• suddenly my uncle gave me the controls
• slowly felt more confident
After the challenge
• loved it
• ⁴ _____

WRITING TIME

5 Write a blog post with a description of Toby's personal challenge. Look at his notes in Exercise 4.

1 Find ideas
Make notes about:
• why he wanted to do the challenge.
• what the challenge was like.
• how Toby felt after the experience.

2 Plan and write
• Organise your ideas into paragraphs. Use Antje's blog post in Exercise 2 to help you.
• Write a draft of your blog post.

3 Check
• Check language: have you used verbs to express emotions?
• Check grammar: have you used a variety of past tenses?
• Write the final version of your blog post.

I can write a description of a personal challenge.

My Language File

WORDLIST 🔊 1.4

Adjectives of emotion
- anxious (adj) _____
- calm (adj) _____
- cheerful (adj) _____
- confused (adj) _____
- delighted (adj) _____
- disappointed (adj) _____
- exhausted (adj) _____
- pleased (adj) _____
- stressed (adj) _____
- surprised (adj) _____
- upset (adj) _____

Verbs of success and failure
- achieve (v) _____
- aim (v) _____
- fail (v) _____
- improve (v) _____
- manage (v) _____
- reach (v) _____
- succeed (v) _____

Achieving goals
- break down (v) _____
- get on with (v) _____
- give up (v) _____
- keep on (v) _____
- put off (v) _____
- work out (v) _____

Word friends (achieving goals)
- do your best _____
- get something right/wrong _____
- get things done _____
- give something a go _____
- make decisions _____
- make mistakes _____
- make progress _____
- make the most of something _____
- take it easy _____
- take something seriously _____

Immigration
- arrival (n) _____
- explore (v) _____
- face challenges _____
- immigrant (n) _____
- migrant (n) _____
- miss (v) _____
- population (n) _____
- stereotype (n) _____
- support (v) _____
- translate (v) _____

Personality adjectives
- active (adj) _____
- competitive (adj) _____
- creative (adj) _____
- curious (adj) _____
- generous (adj) _____
- gentle (adj) _____
- organised (adj) _____
- patient (adj) _____
- reliable (adj) _____
- sensible (adj) _____

Extra words
- accent (n) _____
- adventure (n) _____
- advice (n) _____
- basic English _____
- brave (adj) _____
- confident (adj) _____
- courage (n) _____
- cry (v) _____
- culture (n) _____
- discover (v) _____
- experience (n) _____
- fear of failure _____
- find things hard _____
- fresh ideas (n) _____
- fresh start (n) _____
- get better/worse at something _____
- goal (n) _____
- gradually (adv) _____
- impossible (adj) _____
- in a rush _____
- join a club _____
- limit (n) _____
- make friends _____
- move to another country _____
- need a hand _____
- poor background _____
- proud (adj) _____
- responsibility (n) _____
- result (n) _____
- routine (n) _____
- scared of heights _____
- scream (v) _____
- set my alarm _____
- shake (v) _____
- share (v) _____
- shiver (v) _____
- shout (v) _____
- solution (n) _____
- stay positive _____
- step by step _____
- suffer (from) (v) _____
- sweat (v) _____
- take something up (v) _____
- target (n) _____
- workshop (n) _____

Sounds good!
- I'm impressed! _____
- A complete failure! _____
- I admit it. _____
- So true! _____

MY LANGUAGE NOTES

My favourite words/expressions from this unit

Unit 1

Self-check

Vocabulary

1 Choose the correct option.
1. I was *surprised / exhausted* when he said that.
2. I felt *cheerful / anxious* before the test.
3. We all *make / do* mistakes sometimes. The important thing is to learn from them.
4. Our teacher likes us to be *curious / patient* in class and ask lots of questions.
5. James is *gentle / generous*. He always gives tips.
6. Work hard and I'm sure you'll *achieve / succeed*.
7. Why not just give it a *go / come*? You might like it!
8. I like the way Hannah just gets things *done / do* without complaining.

2 Complete the sentences with the prepositions below.

> down   off   on   out   up   with

1. Don't give _____ just because it's difficult.
2. I can't work _____ this problem.
3. I know I need to start this essay, but I keep putting it _____ .
4. If you keep _____ working like this, you'll get a good grade this year.
5. We can't keep chatting. We need to get on _____ the task.
6. If you break the work _____ into smaller parts, you might find it easier.

3 Choose the correct option.

Maya: How is your new life in Australia, Adam?
Adam: It's great. There's a big British ¹*population / people* here.
Maya: I see. Are there a lot of British ²*arrivals / immigrants* where you live?
Adam: Yes, there are. It's useful when you first arrive – there's a lot of ³*stereotype / support*. But to be honest, I'd like to travel and ⁴*explore / miss* the rest of Australia.
Maya: Yes, I can imagine. And what sort of challenges do you ⁵*get / face*?
Adam: Oh, the weather. It's too hot!
Maya: Ha! It's cold and rainy here in the UK this week, so don't complain!
Adam: Yes, that's true. I don't really ⁶*lose / miss* the British winter!

Grammar

4 Complete the sentences with the Present Simple or Present Continuous form of the verbs in brackets.
1. We _____ (stay) in a hotel at the moment, until we can move into our new house.
2. Jake _____ (get up) at 6 a.m. every morning.
3. Can I call you back? I _____ (have) lunch at the moment.
4. Sally _____ (not enjoy) this film and wants to leave the cinema.
5. _____ (your mum/like) her new job?

5 Complete the text with the Past Simple, Past Continuous or Present Perfect form of the verbs in brackets.

We ¹_____ (not be) to many places outside the UK, so last summer my parents ²_____ (decide) to travel around Italy by train. It was one of the best experiences I ³_____ (ever/have). Travelling by train in a different country ⁴_____ (be) really exciting! We ⁵_____ (see) lots of great places and ⁶_____ (talk) to lots of interesting people, but it ⁷_____ (not be) all good. While we ⁸_____ (walk) around Rome, Mum lost her bag with all her money and her passport! We spent the next day at the embassy, getting a new one. While we ⁹_____ (wait) there, we ¹⁰_____ (meet) a friend of Mum's who invited us to stay with her for the rest of the week!

Speaking

6 Complete the dialogues with one word in each gap.
1. A: Excuse me, would you _____ helping me?
   B: Of course not.
2. A: Can I _____ you anything?
   B: No, I'm fine, but thanks anyway.
3. A: Can I _____ you a hand?
   B: That's really nice of you, thanks.
4. A: Could you help me with this?
   B: Sure! I'll be with you in a _____ .
5. A: Can you help me with something?
   B: Of course! What _____ I do for you?

YOUR SCORE

Vocabulary: __/20   Speaking: __/5
Grammar: __/15   Total: __/40

Clean and green!

2

VOCABULARY
Talking about the environment | Compound nouns: the environment | Protecting and damaging the environment | Environmental issues | Elections and campaigns

GRAMMAR
Past Perfect | Used to and Past Simple

2.1 Vocabulary
Protecting the environment

1 ● Read the sentences and write the missing environment words in the crossword.
1 _____ is a great solution for countries surrounded by the sea.
2 Did you know you can recycle _____ to grow plants?
3 That's the _____ where they make cars.
4 The government needs to do more to reduce _____.
5 Global warming is caused by too much carbon in the Earth's _____.

Crossword:
1. w i n d _ p o w e r
2. f o _ d _ _ a _ t
3. f _ _ t _ r
4. p _ _ l _ t _ n
5. a _ _ _ s _ h _ e

2 ●● Choose the correct option.
1 We need more trees on the planet because they produce (oxygen) / pollution.
2 Solar / Wind power isn't really possible in this part of the country because it's so dark all the time.
3 The company closed the factory / atmosphere after complaints about pollution from local residents.
4 It's becoming more and more difficult to find new sources of petrol / oil in the world.
5 Does your car run on oil / petrol or gas?
6 The forest fire was in an area with lots of endangered / wind animals.

3 ● **WORD FRIENDS** Match verbs 1–5 with their opposites a–e.
1 [d] recycle/reuse   a clean up
2 [ ] protect   b waste
3 [ ] pollute   c damage
4 [ ] save   d ~~throw away~~
5 [ ] reduce   e increase

4 ● Match the sentence halves.
1 [b] We need to reduce the amount of carbon
2 [ ] Because of global
3 [ ] We need to use more types of renewable
4 [ ] It's incredible that some people don't believe that climate
5 [ ] We take our bottles and cans to a recycling
6 [ ] Driving an electric
7 [ ] What are the main energy

a change is real.
b ~~dioxide in the atmosphere~~.
c sources used to generate electricity in this country?
d car is a good way to reduce pollution.
e warming, many parts of the world are seeing water shortages.
f energy, such as wind and solar power.
g centre next to the supermarket.

5 ●● Complete the sentences with the words below.

> change   dioxide   endangered   factories   oil
> oxygen   pollution   recycling   ~~solar~~   source

1 Getting energy from the sun as *solar* power is a great way to reduce _____.

2 Using _____ as an energy source is one of the biggest causes of climate _____.

3 Trees take in carbon _____ and release _____ into the atmosphere.

4 Our city needs more _____ centres. In fact, a lot of things that people throw away could be used as an energy _____.

5 Water and land pollution from the _____ in the area affects _____ animals.

6 ●● Choose the word or phrase that does NOT fit in each sentence.

1 Do you ____ plastic bags at home?
   a reuse   (b) pollute   c throw away
2 What do people in your country do to ____ the environment?
   a recycle   b protect   c damage
3 The main aim of our green group is to protect ____.
   a rubbish   b the environment
   c people's health
4 Personally, I don't do much to ____ beaches.
   a pollute   b clean up   c waste
5 My school ____ a lot of energy every month.
   a throws away   b saves   c wastes
6 The company's actions do a lot to ____ pollution.
   a increase   b waste   c decrease

7 ●● The words in bold in the sentences are wrong. Correct them.

1 Let's take these newspapers and magazines to the recycling **factory**. *centre*
2 The local government has decided to clean **out** the local beaches. _____
3 Throwing away plastic bags and other rubbish **protects** the environment. _____
4 I listened to a talk last night about climate **energy** – it's a huge problem. _____
5 These factories have caused a lot of air **rubbish**. _____
6 Unfortunately, over 1,000 plants and animals in the USA are **renewable**. _____

8 ●●● Complete the words in the text.

The time for change is now

It's important to understand why people should ¹p*rotect* the planet more. It's a really big problem, and we are already seeing the effects of climate ²c_____. Although ³e_____ cars are a bit better for the environment, they're too expensive for most people, so a lot of people still drive cars which use ⁴p_____ and even fewer people use public transport or cycle to work. People should also think about what they eat. Meat and dairy farming ⁵d_____ the environment and ⁶w_____ a lot of energy, so adding more plants to our diet can help. And we ⁷t_____ away plastic bags and aluminium cans which we should ⁸r_____. We need to move to ⁹r_____ energy and stop depending on petrol and ¹⁰o_____. We need to ¹¹c_____ up the oceans and the air. And we need to do it now or our children may not have a planet to live in.

I can talk about pollution and the environment.

2.2 Grammar
Past Perfect

GRAMMAR › Past Perfect

Past Perfect
He **had collected** a container of waste.
I **hadn't realised** what it looked like.
Had this idea **helped**? Yes, it **had**./No, it **hadn't**.

Past Perfect and Past Simple
When I **got** there, the zoo-keeper **had just fed** them.
He**'d already mixed** the waste with water **before** I **arrived**.
I **left** the zoo after we**'d had** lunch.

Time expressions
when, before, after, just, already, by the time

1 ● Complete the sentences with the Past Perfect form of the verbs in brackets.

1 By the time she was twenty-five, Silvia *had travelled* (travel) all over the world.
2 They were hungry because they _____ (not eat) their breakfast.
3 _____ (you/finish) your homework before you went out last night?
4 Five minutes into the film, I realised I _____ (see) it before.
5 _____ (you/try) Mexican food before you went to that restaurant?
6 James was pleased when he changed class because he _____ (not be) happy in his old class.

2 ●● Complete the sentences with the Past Perfect form of the verbs below.

| already/leave | ~~close~~ | forget | never/see |
| not buy | not realise | | |

1 We arrived late at the zoo and it *had closed.*
2 Miguel _____ how much work he still had to do on his History project.
3 When I arrived at the party, Julia _____ .
4 When I got to class, I realised I _____ to bring my homework.
5 Jack and Fiona couldn't go to the concert because they _____ any tickets.
6 Chiara _____ a volcano before she went to Indonesia.

3 ● Choose the correct option.

1 We were very tired because we *went* / (*had gone*) to bed late the night before.
2 Had you ever visited a national park before you *went* / *had been* to South Africa?
3 We *waited* / *had waited* in line for two hours when the ticket office finally opened.
4 I *had already read* / *already read* the book, so I knew how the film ended.

4 ●● Use the prompts to make sentences. Use the Past Perfect and the Past Simple.

1 Angela / not study / English / before / she / visit / London
Angela hadn't studied English before she visited London.
2 by the time / I / finish / school yesterday / it / get / dark outside
_____
3 how long / you / have / your bike / when / somebody / steal / it / ?
_____
4 I / just / arrived / at the party / when / it / finish
_____
5 Kayla / be / tired / because / she / not sleep / well
_____

5 ●● Complete the blog post with the time expressions below.

| after | already | ~~before~~ | by the time | just |

Worst day ever today!
I got up late and ¹*before* I went downstairs to have breakfast, everybody had eaten all the pancakes my mum had made. ² _____ I had made my own breakfast (cereal ☹), I got dressed quickly and left for school. I had ³ _____ walked out of the door when it started raining. And guess what: I didn't have an umbrella. Then my bus got stuck in traffic, so ⁴ _____ I arrived at school, classes had ⁵ _____ started. The teacher was really annoyed with me and said that I had to read a whole unit of the book. I had to stay in class during break to finish it.

2.3 Reading and Vocabulary
A trip to the countryside

1 Choose the correct option.
1. There are many *environmental* / *waste* organisations around the world which aim to protect natural habitats.
2. It's important to *leave* / *respect* the countryside and take your rubbish with you when you go home.
3. The Lake District is *a national* / *an international* park in the north of England.
4. Can you clean up your *mess* / *wildlife*, please?
5. When you visit the countryside, it's important to leave no *shape* / *trace*.
6. We try to recycle as much rubbish as we can, to stop it going to a waste *place* / *dump*.

2 Read the article. How did the writer spend most of their time on holiday? Choose the correct answer.
  a going hiking
  b eating in cafés
  c collecting rubbish

3 Read the article again and choose the correct answer.
1. What does the writer say about their friends' house?
   a They visit it every summer.
   b They remember visiting it as a child.
   c They went sailing there last year.
2. What did the writer's parents teach them?
   a not to leave anything in the countryside
   b to show them respect
   c how to walk in the countryside
3. What is fly-camping?
   a camping in different places
   b taking all your stuff home with you when you go camping
   c buying basic camping equipment to dispose of rather than carry home
4. Why did they go into the village?
   a to buy food
   b to dispose of the rubbish
   c to have lunch
5. What did the café owner tell them?
   a The situation had improved recently.
   b The situation had worsened recently.
   c The situation had always been bad.

The clean-up trip

Last summer I went on holiday with my family to our friends' summer house in the countryside, near a national park. We used to go there every year when we were little, but we hadn't been back for years. I had really fond memories of the place as a young child, sailing on the lake and walking through the fields nearby. When we were little, our parents had always taught us to respect the countryside and wildlife and leave no trace, and that's what we always did.

On the first morning after we arrived, we decided to go hiking around the lake. But instead of the beautiful area I remembered, it was just a mess. It looked like people had camped near the lake and just left all their stuff there. I had read about this before: it's called 'fly-camping'. Instead of staying at campsites, people who fly-camp want to travel light, so they only buy basic camping equipment, then just leave all their stuff there in the wild, like disposable items, so they don't have to take it home with them.

We picked up what rubbish we could and took it into the local village to throw it away properly. While we were there, we decided to have lunch at a café and spoke to the owner. We told her about how we had visited here when we were younger and how it hadn't been a problem then. 'It's got really bad over the last few years. It's almost like people think it's a waste dump,' she said. 'The other day, I was walking my dog over there and he came running back to me. He had found some food containers, and one of them had stuck to his face and he couldn't get it off. Poor thing.' She also said she'd reported it to an environmental organisation, but they hadn't been able to do anything yet.

After that, we decided to spend another day picking up the rubbish we found. We used some big bags we had brought from the village and filled them up every day. I hope the situation gets better in the future.

I can understand a story about the environment.

2.4 Grammar

Used to and Past Simple

GRAMMAR — Used to and Past Simple

Used to and Past Simple
Our street *used to be* full of traffic. (past state/situation)
Our street *was* full of traffic.
We *didn't use to go* outside much. (past habit/regular action)
We *didn't go* outside much.
Did you *use to play* here?   Yes, I *did*./No, I *didn't*.
Where *did* he *use to play*?

Past Simple
I *spoke* to him yesterday. (single action in the past)

1 ● Match the sentence halves.
1. [d] I didn't use to like many vegetables,
2. [ ] We used to throw away all our rubbish,
3. [ ] We used to use a lot of oil for fuel in my country,
4. [ ] Sara didn't use to work hard at school,
5. [ ] Paula used to throw away litter,

a but now she studies all the time.
b but now we use more renewable energy.
c but now she always puts it in the recycling bin.
d but now I like most of them.
e but these days we recycle nearly everything.

2 ●● Complete the sentences with the correct form of *used to* and the verbs below.

| be   live   not have   not watch   play   travel |

1 My dad *used to play* football for a club when he was younger.
2 Where _____ (you) before you moved to this street?
3 My grandparents _____ TV much when they were children.
4 We _____ a recycling centre in our town, so it was difficult to recycle anything.
5 We _____ everywhere by car, but now we use public transport a lot more.
6 _____ (there) a lot of smoke in the air here before they closed the factory?

3 ●● Rewrite the sentences using *used to*.
1 When I was little, I played with toys every day.
   When I was little, I used to play with toys every day.
2 My grandparents' generation didn't recycle rubbish.
   _____
3 Did you play video games every day when you were younger?
   _____
4 When he was my age, my dad worked in a shop at the weekend.
   _____
5 My aunt lived on a boat when she was a teenager.
   _____

4 ●●● Complete the text with the correct form of *used to* or the Past Simple and the verbs in brackets. If both are possible, use *used to*.

RECYCLING through the ages

Many people think that recycling is a new thing, but in fact, some people [1] *used to recycle* (recycle) things in 400 BC! Scientists recently [2]_____ (discover) that people in Turkey reused glass thousands of years ago. And in 1031, the Japanese [3]_____ (recycle) paper for the first time.

In times when people were poor, they [4]_____ (not throw) things away. Just before the industrial revolution (1760–1830), people [5]_____ (melt) and recycle metals. But during the industrial revolution, things suddenly [6]_____ (become) cheaper and easier to make, so there was less recycling.

Nowadays, we recycle because we know more about environmental problems. So while our ancestors [7]_____ (recycle) because they had to, we now recycle because we should.

I can use *used to* and the Past Simple to talk about past habits and states.

2.5 Listening and Vocabulary
Elections, campaigns and the environment

1 **WORD FRIENDS** Complete the words in the sentences.

1 Every year we have the chance to v o_ t_ e_ for a new class president.
2 Our group is going to o_ _ _ _ _ _ _ an event at school to raise money for environmental projects.
3 The government has decided to h_ _ _ _ an election this May.
4 Jackie wants us to s_ _ _ _ a p_ _ _ _ _ _ _ to stop the company building a factory in this area.
5 After seeing how polluted the ocean was, I decided to j_ _ _ _ a campaign to raise awareness of the problem.
6 My dad advised me to b_ _ _ _ _ _ a member of an environmental group if I want to do something to help the environment.

2 Find the words below in the word search. Look →, ↓, ↗ and ↘.

~~campaign~~ candidate election event join member organise petition sign vote

P	E	T	I	T	I	O	N	N	D	E	M
M	D	R	K	C	T	K	O	G	S	V	E
C	J	C	A	N	D	I	D	A	T	E	M
A	Z	V	N	V	T	W	V	J	V	N	B
M	G	L	O	C	M	O	P	O	Y	T	E
P	G	I	E	V	K	R	L	R	T	P	R
A	X	L	N	X	L	G	E	K	N	E	G
I	E	Y	Q	N	Q	A	V	S	G	T	N
G	S	G	Q	X	M	N	K	Z	U	I	I
N	D	I	X	N	Q	I	H	I	O	N	H
K	J	P	G	M	A	S	K	J	G	V	T
W	Y	X	Z	N	J	E	G	O	B	A	V

3 🔊 2.1 Listen to four dialogues and choose the correct answer.

1 What did Tara do in the holidays?
A ☐ B ☐ C ☐

2 What has Tyler James done?
A ☐ B ☐ C ☐

3 What activity will Kerry's group do next?
A ☐ B ☐ C ☐

4 What does Paul think we need more of?
A ☐ B ☐ C ☐

4 🔊 2.1 Listen again. Mark the sentences T (true) or F (false).

1 ☐ Tara's friend didn't know what a green camp was.
2 ☐ At green camp, they learned about protecting animals and the environment.
3 ☐ Tyler James has always been very 'green'.
4 ☐ Kerry's dad thinks she did a good thing at school today.
5 ☐ Paul thinks all cars make the air dirty.

I can understand conversations about elections and campaigns.

2.6 Speaking
Agreeing and disagreeing

1 🔊 **2.2** Listen and repeat the phrases.

SPEAKING — Agreeing and disagreeing

Agreeing
I think that's a good/great idea.
I think so too.
Absolutely! I (totally) agree.
You can say that again!

Partially agreeing
Maybe you're right, but what can we do?
You've got a point, but it's very difficult.
True, but is there a better idea?
I suppose so/not.
I guess so/not.

Disagreeing
I don't agree.   I (totally) disagree.
I don't think we should do that.   I don't think so.
I'm not sure about that.   That's not always true.

2 Match the sentence halves.
1 c Maybe you're
2 ☐ I totally
3 ☐ That's not
4 ☐ I'm not
5 ☐ I think that's a
6 ☐ Really? I

a sure about that.
b don't agree.
c ~~right, but what else is there?~~
d agree.
e great idea.
f always true.

3 Order the words to make sentences.
1 think / too / I / so
   I think so too.
2 should / I / we / think / don't / that / do
   _____
3 disagree / I / totally
   _____
4 that / say / again / can / you / !
   _____
5 so / suppose / I
   _____
6 so / I / think / don't
   _____

4 🔊 **2.3** Complete the dialogue with one word in each gap. Then listen and check.

Kayla: OK, let's get started. So what ideas do we have for the class environmental project?
Dan: Well, I thought we could organise a garage sale to raise money for an environmental organisation.
Kayla: I'm not ¹*sure* about that. I mean, the idea is to do something that the whole class can get involved in rather than just raise money for a charity.
Anne: Yes, I ²_____ so too, Kayla.
Dan: Maybe you're ³_____, but what can we do?
Anne: I thought we could give a presentation on different ways to save energy at home.
Dan: Hmm … Well, you've got a ⁴_____ about involving people, but I don't think we ⁵_____ limit ourselves like that. What about something where we take direct action? Could we go and collect plastic bags and aluminium cans, then recycle them?
Anne: I think that ⁶_____ a great idea. Also, any money we make, we can donate to an environmental organisation, like you wanted to, Dan.
Kayla: Absolutely! I totally ⁷_____. This is going to be a great project!
Anne: You can say that ⁸_____!

Unit 2 | 22 | I can agree and disagree with other people.

On the Portal
Extra Practice Activities: Lesson 2.6

2.7 Writing
A survey report

1 Complete the survey report with these words.

| ~~aim~~ | almost | class | few | found | half | have |
| participated | quarters | surprisingly |

How much do you know about rubbish in the street?

Objective

The [1] *aim* of the survey was to find out how much students know about rubbish in the street. We asked eight questions. Twenty-five students from our class [2] _____.

Survey results by question

1 Do you notice rubbish in the street?
Only a few students notice rubbish in the street.

2 Do you drop rubbish in the street?
[3] _____ of the class say they sometimes drop rubbish in the street, especially sweet wrappers.

3 Have you ever picked up rubbish someone else has dropped in the street?
Nobody in the [4] _____ has ever picked up someone else's rubbish.

4 Have you ever participated in a local project to clean up rubbish?
Three students [5] _____ been on a project to clean up rubbish.

5 Would you participate in a local project to clean up rubbish?
All students say they would participate in such a project.

6 Is there a lot of rubbish in the street in your area?
[6] _____ all the class say there is too much.

7 Do you think people should pay high fines for dropping rubbish in the street?
About three [7] _____ of the class say no. Some students say it is the responsibility of the local council.

8 Can you help reduce the amount of rubbish in the street?
All participants say they can help reduce the amount of rubbish in the street.

Summary conclusions

In conclusion, we [8] _____ that most students didn't really notice rubbish in the street. [9] _____, half of the class said they sometimes dropped rubbish in the street. Only a [10] _____ students had been on a local project to clean up rubbish. The good news is that all students thought they could help reduce the amount of rubbish and would participate in a project to clean it up.

2 Match the quantifiers with the percentages below.

| 100% | 98% | 80% | 75% | 50% | ~~35%~~ | 10% | 0% |

1 some *35%*
2 a few ____
3 half ____
4 none ____
5 many/most ____
6 all ____
7 almost all ____
8 three quarters ____

3 Read the data about thirty other participants who did the same survey. Choose the correct option.

Question 1	Question 2	Question 3	Question 4
50% notice	10% have	35% have	0% have
Question 5	Question 6	Question 7	Question 8
75% would	90% too much	98% should pay	100% can

1 (Half) / Three quarters of them notice rubbish in the street.
2 Many / A few students drop rubbish in the street.
3 Some / Most students have picked up someone else's rubbish.
4 Everybody / Nobody has participated in a local project to clean up rubbish.
5 Three quarters / Almost all of them would participate in a local project.
6 A few / Most of the participants say there is too much rubbish in the streets.
7 Almost all / Three quarters of them say yes.
8 All / None of the participants say they can help reduce the amount of rubbish in the street.

WRITING TIME

4 Write a survey report. Use the data in Exercise 3.

1 Find ideas
Make notes about:
- your objective.
- your findings.
- your summary conclusions.

2 Plan and write
- Organise your ideas into three sections. Use the report in Exercise 1 to help you.
- Write a draft of your report.

3 Check
- Check language: have you used quantifiers and percentages?
- Check grammar: have you used the correct tense for each section?
- Write the final version of your report.

My Language File

WORDLIST 🔊 2.4

Talking about the environment
- atmosphere (n) _____
- endangered animal (n) _____
- factory (n) _____
- food waste (n) _____
- oil (n) _____
- oxygen (n) _____
- petrol (n) _____
- pollution (n) _____
- solar power (n) _____
- wind power (n) _____

Compound nouns: the environment
- carbon dioxide (n) _____
- climate change (n) _____
- electric car (n) _____
- energy source (n) _____
- global warming (n) _____
- recycling centre (n) _____
- renewable energy (n) _____

Word friends
(protecting and damaging the environment)
- clean up rivers _____
- damage the planet _____
- increase pollution _____
- pollute the air _____
- protect the environment _____
- recycle plastic bags _____
- reduce food waste _____
- reuse aluminium cans _____
- save energy _____
- throw away rubbish _____
- waste water _____

Environmental issues
- environmental organisation (n) _____
- leave no trace _____

- mess (n) _____
- national park (n) _____
- respect the countryside _____
- respect wildlife _____
- waste dump (n) _____

Word friends
(elections and campaigns)
- become a member of _____
- hold an election _____
- join a campaign _____
- organise an event _____
- sign a petition _____
- vote for a candidate _____

Extra words
- bike lane (n) _____
- bin (n) _____
- biogas (n) _____
- breathe (v) _____
- campfire (n) _____
- campsite (n) _____
- cardboard (n) _____
- careful (about/with) (adj) _____
- charge a battery _____
- coal (n) _____
- compost (n) _____
- countryside (n) _____
- create green spaces _____
- creature (n) _____
- crisp packet (n) _____
- cut down trees _____
- cyclist (n) _____
- design a plan _____
- dryer (n) _____
- encourage (v) _____
- environmentally friendly (adj) _____
- farm animal (n) _____
- in a terrible state _____

- keep the air clean _____
- leave lights on _____
- litter (n) _____
- local council (n) _____
- non-meat product (n) _____
- organise a clean-up _____
- overcrowding (n) _____
- path (n) _____
- pick up rubbish _____
- plant trees _____
- plastic (n) _____
- produce (v) _____
- public transport (n) _____
- release (v) _____
- rubbish bag (n) _____
- share cars _____
- source (n) _____
- stream (n) _____
- survey (n) _____
- switch off lights _____
- toothpaste tube (n) _____
- traffic (n) _____
- trash (n) _____
- turn into (v) _____
- turn off lights _____
- wasteful (adj) _____
- wildlife (n) _____
- zoo-keeper (n) _____

Sounds good!
- So what? _____
- We're way too early. _____
- See? _____

MY LANGUAGE NOTES

My favourite words/expressions from this unit

Unit 2 24

Self-check

Vocabulary

1 Complete the words in the sentences.
1 Local residents have complained about plans to build a new f_ _ _ _ _ _ in the area.
2 Try to cook smaller meals in order to reduce food w_ _ _ _.
3 Electric cars p_ _ _ _ _ _ _ _ _ the environment much less than traditional petrol cars.
4 There was very little rain this summer, which d_ _ _ _ _ _ _ lots of plants in the area.
5 Let's take all these plastic bottles to the r_ _ _ _ _ _ _ _ _ c_ _ _ _ _ _.
6 Using oil as an energy source pollutes the a_ _ _ _ _ _ _ _ _ _ _.

2 Complete the sentences with one word in each gap.
1 People throw _____ too much stuff! We need to recycle as much as we can.
2 WWF is an organisation which works to protect endangered _____.
3 Many scientists agree that _____ change is the biggest problem in the world today.
4 This machine measures the level of _____ dioxide in the air.
5 Turn the light off when you leave the room. Don't _____ energy.
6 Wind power is a very cheap form of renewable _____.

3 Choose the correct option.
1 Would you like to drive an *electric / energy* car?
2 We always reuse plastic *bags / waste* from the supermarket.
3 Many countries are looking for new energy *centres / sources* which are cleaner.
4 Can you take these bottles to the recycling *centre / change* while you're out?
5 Somebody needs to clean *up / down* this beach!
6 This government aims to *recycle / reduce* pollution by ninety percent by 2040.
7 Would you *write / sign* this petition to protect natural habitats in the area?
8 This year our school is going to *make / hold* an election for the student council.

Grammar

4 Complete the text with the Past Perfect form of the verbs below.

agree   be   collect   do   drop   get up   organise

Yesterday evening I was tired because I ¹_____ at 5 a.m. My friends ²_____ a trip to the park to clean up the litter and I ³_____ to help. When we got there, we realised there ⁴_____ a huge event there because it was an absolute mess! We couldn't believe what those people ⁵_____ to our park. They ⁶_____ rubbish everywhere. We worked all day and by the time we had finished, we ⁷_____ fifty bags of rubbish!

5 Complete the sentences with the correct form of *used to* or the Past Simple and the verbs in brackets. If both are possible, use *used to*.
1 Last year we _____ (win) an award.
2 Sally _____ (not care) about the environment, but she does now.
3 I _____ (recycle) a lot less than I do now.
4 _____ (Jo/help) clean up the park yesterday?
5 We _____ (not have) a recycling centre in our town.
6 _____ (Luke/be) a member of the Clean up Our Town campaign?
7 We _____ (not learn) about saving water today – that was yesterday.
8 _____ (you/leave) the lights on?

Speaking

6 Complete the dialogues with one word in each gap.
1 A: I don't think climate change is real.
   B: I _____ disagree!
2 A: This environmental project is brilliant.
   B: You can _____ that again!
3 A: I don't think we can improve it.
   B: Really? I don't _____.
4 A: I don't think our idea is going to work.
   B: I guess _____.
5 A: We can do more to protect the environment.
   B: I _____ so too.

YOUR SCORE

Vocabulary: __/20   Speaking: __/5
Grammar: __/15   Total: __/40

Looking good

3

VOCABULARY
Clothes and accessories | Adjectives to describe clothes and accessories | Appearance | Fashion | Parts of clothes and shoes

GRAMMAR
Present Perfect Continuous | Present Perfect Simple and Continuous

3.1 Vocabulary
Clothes and appearance

1 ● Write the words below in the correct column.

ankle boots	bracelet	cap	chain	elbow pads
knee pads	leggings	mask	ring	sandals
shoulder pads	suit	tights		

Hands/Arms	
Legs	
Feet	ankle boots
Head/Neck	
Whole body	

2 ●● Write the correct word for each definition.
1. You wear these on your feet in the summer. s*andals*
2. You wear this on your head when you play some sports. c_____
3. This is a piece of jewellery on your finger. r_____
4. This is a piece of jewellery around your wrist. b_____
5. These are tight and you wear them on your legs. l_____
6. This is a thin gold or silver chain to wear around the neck. n_____

3 ● Choose the odd one out.
1. terrific (leather) fashionable smart
2. colourful loose gold silver
3. denim linen cotton checked
4. cotton terrific old-fashioned ordinary
5. plain scruffy striped checked
6. casual neat silver scruffy

4 ●● Label the photos with a word from box A and a noun from box B.

A
| colourful | denim | gold | leather | smart | striped |

B
| ankle boots | bracelet | cap | chain | leggings | suit |

1. a *smart suit*
2. a _____ 
3. a _____ 
4. _____ 
5. _____
6. a _____ 

Unit 3 26

5 Put the adjectives in brackets in the correct order.

1 Jill has some <u>old-fashioned, plain, leather</u> sandals. (plain, leather, old-fashioned)
2 Will is wearing a _____ suit. (blue, smart, striped)
3 Andrea hates her _____ tights. (scruffy, green, loose)
4 Where are my _____ leggings? (striped, tight, cotton)
5 Katy loves wearing her _____ ankle boots. (silver, fashionable, checked)

6 **WORD FRIENDS** Complete the sentences with the correct form of *be*, *have* or *wear*.

1 Katie <u>has</u> freckles on her face.
2 I think Richard _____ in his twenties.
3 Are you going to _____ a costume to the party?
4 We're not allowed to _____ jewellery at school.
5 I _____ pale skin and brown hair.
6 Jamie _____ very good-looking!
7 I _____ very slim in this photo.

7 Complete the sentences with the correct form of *be*, *have* or *wear*. Then choose the correct option.

1 Dana <u>has</u> painted nails and she's wearing (*gold and silver, checked*) / *checked, gold and silver* leggings.
2 John is in his *thirties* / *threes* and he _____ well-built.
3 My dad always wears a smart, plain *costume* / *suit* to work and he never _____ jewellery.
4 Does your sister _____ *dyed* / *died* hair and _____ *fashionable* / *scruffy* jewellery?
5 Look at these awful *checked, leather* / *leather, checked* sandals! Who would ever _____ them?

8 Look at the pictures and complete the words in the texts.

Maisha

My cousin Maisha is very active. She runs every day and plays lots of sport. She's wearing ¹c a su a l, ²f___r__ leggings and ³k____ p____. I don't think I've ever seen her wear clothes not made for sport! When she isn't dressed for skateboarding, she wears an old, ⁴s___f__ sports kit at home. You can tell she does a lot of sport. She's ⁵a__er__ge h____gh__ and very ⁶s____m.

Joel

My uncle Joel works in an investment company, so he dresses well for work. He always wears a ⁷s____ and ⁸l__t____ shoes to work. He has ⁹p__e skin and lots of ¹⁰f_____l__s on his face, and I think he's very ¹¹g___d-l____n__.

Amanda

My cousin Amanda is in her teens and she always wears ¹² f__h_____bl__ clothes. She has ¹³ d_____ hair and loves wearing colourful ¹⁴ j____l___r like rings and bracelets. In this photo, she's wearing ¹⁵ c_____d leggings and really cool, red ¹⁶ s_____l.

I can describe clothes, accessories and appearance.

3.2 Grammar
Present Perfect Continuous

GRAMMAR Present Perfect Continuous

I**'ve been seeing** a lot more posts from influencers.
I **haven't been working** for money.
How long **have** you **been working** for this company?

Time expressions
recently, lately, all day/night
Recently they've been sharing video reviews.

since last Friday/October/Saturday/I woke up
I've been using a new social media platform **since** last summer.

for two hours/three years/a long time/ages
Nina has been helping me **for** a few days.

1 ● Complete the sentences with the Present Perfect Continuous form of the verbs in brackets.
   1 Josy should relax this evening. She'**s been revising** (revise) for her test all day.
   2 Julia _____ (not write) her fashion blog much.
   3 We _____ (read) the product reviews on her channel for years.
   4 How long _____ (they/collect) vintage fashion magazines?
   5 Kevin _____ (listen) to the same playlist for three days!

2 ● Write the phrases below in the correct column.

   | a long time   afternoon   ages   four months |
   | I got home   last Tuesday   morning   night |
   | two o'clock |

for	since	all
a long time		

3 ●● Complete the sentences with the Present Perfect Continuous form of the verbs below. There is one extra verb.

   | look   make   not practise   save   tidy   ~~wear~~ |

   1 I'**ve been wearing** glasses for four months.
   2 Tara _____ the piano much recently.
   3 How long _____ (Lucy) for a job as an influencer?
   4 I'm tired! We _____ the garden for hours now!
   5 How long _____ (you) your own clothes?

4 ●● Complete the second sentence with the word in bold so that it means the same as the first one. Use no more than five words.
   1 We started writing this review at 4 p.m. and it's 7 p.m. now.
      We've **been writing this review for** three hours. **FOR**
   2 Sara moved here in January and she lives here now.
      Sara _____ January. **LIVING**
   3 What did you do from 9 a.m. until now?
      What _____ all morning? **DOING**
   4 Tom didn't post on his channel last week or this week.
      Tom _____ on his channel recently. **BEEN**
   5 They started trying on clothes at 10 a.m. and it's 3 p.m. now.
      They've been _____. **AGES**

5 ●●● Complete the text with one word in each gap.

   I never used to be interested in fashion, but recently I've been ¹ *wearing* much more fashionable clothes. It all started a few months ago, when my friend Jana saw me at school and said, 'Kate, have you been to the second-hand shop in town? It's been there ² _____ a while now! Let's go there together.' I agreed: 'You're right – I do need some new clothes and I ³ _____ been putting off getting some ⁴ _____ last year.'

   We had a great day. When we got home, we were exhausted and there were bags everywhere. My mum said 'What have you ⁵ _____ doing? What is all this mess?'

   Now I'm really into fashion and I ⁶ _____ been experimenting with a fashion vlog ⁷ _____ the last three months. My followers tell me they've ⁸ _____ enjoying it. One person asked me, 'How ⁹ _____ have you been making fashion videos?' and couldn't believe it when I told her it had only been three months. She thinks I've been studying fashion ¹⁰ _____ my life!

Unit 3   28   I can use the Present Perfect Continuous to talk about things that started in the past and have continued until now.

On the Portal
Extra Practice Activities: Lesson 3.2

3.3 Reading and Vocabulary
Trends in fashion

1 Match the sentence halves.
1. [b] Many young
2. [ ] Is that a new
3. [ ] One way of reducing waste is clothing
4. [ ] Many high
5. [ ] I like to keep up with the latest key
6. [ ] I don't always follow fashion; I like to have an individual
7. [ ] These trainers are made from ethical
8. [ ] Make clothes your own by adding new

a rental, where you rent clothes for a few days.
b ~~designers these days are experimenting with new types of materials.~~
c trends in fashion.
d look with the clothes I wear.
e features such as zips or pockets.
f outfit? It looks great!
g street stores sell clothes that celebrities wear.
h materials.

2 Read the article quickly. What is it about? Choose the correct answer.
a where to buy clothes
b creating an individual look
c using fashion to make a change

3 Read the article again. Complete the article with sentences a–g. There are two extra sentences.
a This is because they want to show they care about the wider environment.
b This was the start of a more modern way of expressing your beliefs.
c More recently, vegan fashion companies have replaced animal products with plant-based alternatives.
d They were very popular with both men and women at the time.
e And this isn't just a modern trend.
f People can express their beliefs and values in other ways too.
g The clothes you wear might also help to change the industry.

I can understand an article about new trends in fashion.

Fashion, beliefs and values

Speak to anyone in the fashion industry and they'll tell you that fashion is so much more than just the clothes you wear. Key trends in fashion are often not just about creating an individual look, but also about expressing your beliefs and values. [1]___ For example, in seventeenth-century England, men chose to wear short, colourful suits with new features as a political statement against the more traditional politicians of the time.

Across the Atlantic, during the American Revolution, many women chose to avoid buying British products and many groups formed to make their own clothes to show their support for America. [2]___ That's to say making choices based on how and where clothes are made rather than just what they look like. For example, people who care deeply about animal rights have, for a long time, talked about avoiding the use of animal materials in clothes and have protested against fur coats or the use of leather in shoes. [3]___ One example of this is piñatex, a leather alternative made from pineapple leaves. By choosing a new outfit made from more ethical materials such as this, people are able to express their beliefs through the clothes they buy in a less direct, but equally important way.

Consumers are also choosing clothes made through sustainable processes. [4]___ So they choose to buy from companies that respect it. These include companies that cut material in certain ways to avoid waste; or companies that use techniques which apply 100% of the dyes to colour clothes so that nothing is thrown away.

But it's not just about supporting companies that have ethical or sustainable production processes. [5]___ One example of this is avoiding high street stores and buying second-hand clothes. Or simply choosing new clothes because of how long they will last, to avoid having to replace them and producing more waste. Whatever people's reasons are, it's clear that the decisions we make when buying clothes can be powerful statements about what we believe.

3.4 Grammar
Present Perfect Simple and Continuous

GRAMMAR — **Present Perfect Simple and Continuous**

Present Perfect Simple
I've made tablet cases for eight people. (focus on the result)
I haven't found anything I like. (focus on the result)

Present Perfect Continuous
She's been looking for a present for weeks. (focus on the activity)
I've been taking photos of all the cases. (focus on the ongoing action)

For and since
I've been looking for a cool case for my tablet for ages.
I've been very busy since Amy's birthday.

Note: with state verbs (know, understand, etc.), we only use the Present Perfect Simple.

1 ● Match the sentence halves.
1 _b_ Alexa has bought a
2 ___ We've been planning
3 ___ Mum and Dad have told
4 ___ I've made
5 ___ Riley and Ava have known
6 ___ Caleb has been wearing

a each other since primary school.
b ~~costume for the party.~~
c me to wear smarter clothes.
d a bracelet. Do you like it?
e that cap all weekend.
f the fashion show for weeks.

2 ●● Complete the sentences with the Present Perfect Simple or Present Perfect Continuous form of the verbs in brackets.

1 How long _have you been dyeing_ (you/dye) your hair?
2 Kyla _____ (look for) a new raincoat for ages.
3 How long _____ (you/have) those ankle boots?
4 Mum and Dad _____ (talk) about where to go on holiday all morning.
5 I _____ (not post) anything on social media since September.
6 Sally _____ (wear) sandals all summer.

3 ●● Use the prompts to make sentences. Use the Present Perfect Simple or Present Perfect Continuous and add *for* or *since* if necessary.

1 I / send / three emails / today
   I've sent three emails today.
2 how long / you / have / dyed hair / ?
   _____
3 Jia / wear / glasses / January
   _____
4 how long / you / study / fashion / ?
   _____
5 Mark and Jill / like / heavy metal music / years
   _____

4 ●●● Complete the text with the Present Perfect Simple or Present Perfect Continuous form of the verbs below.

| be | ~~buy~~ | make | recycle | send | use | wear |

Action Point Clothing

Imagine the situation. You ¹ _'ve bought_ a new jacket because you ² _____ your old one for years. What happens to your old jacket? Do you throw it away or take it to a charity shop?

One new business in South London has the answer. Action Point Clothing ³ _____ old clothes for five years. They ⁴ _____ over 200 new items of clothing by transforming old clothes into more modern versions. What's more, they ⁵ _____ half of their profits to train young people how to design clothes.

So how does it work? 'We started off with a competition for young people to design clothes and then we used the winning designs on the clothes we received to make them fashionable again,' says company CEO Laura Bauer. 'Since then, there ⁶ _____ no shortage of new designs. The young people at our local school ⁷ _____ us new designs every week!'

I can understand the difference between the Present Perfect Simple and Continuous.

On the Portal
Extra Practice Activities: Lesson 3.4

3.5 Listening and Vocabulary
An eco-fashion show

1 Look at the pictures and complete the crossword.

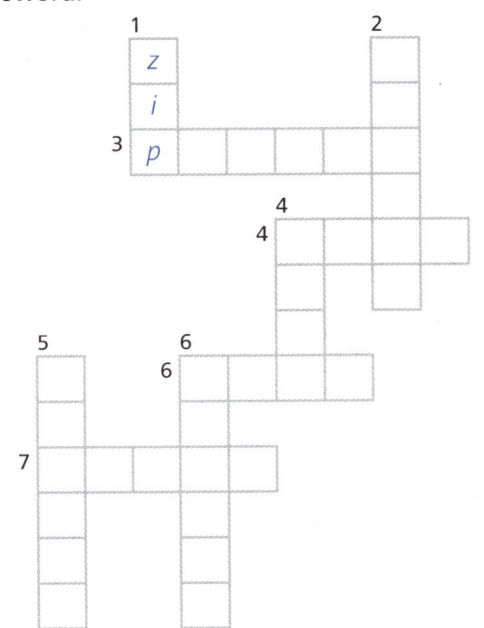

Across
3, 4, 6, 7

Down
1, 2, 4, 5, 6

2 Order the letters and write the words in the sentences.
1. These h*eels* (SHELE) are so high that my shoes make me taller than my brother!
2. Put your h_____ (DOHO) up – it's raining.
3. These shoes are so worn-out! There's a hole in the s_____ (ELOS).
4. Mum, can you help me do up this dress? I think the z_____ (IPZ) is stuck.
5. I really like this shirt, but the s_____ (VESELES) are too long. They come all the way over my hands.
6. Can you carry my phone for me, please? My dress hasn't got a p_____ (TEPKOC).

I can understand a conversation about unusual clothes.

3 🔊 3.1 Listen to an interview with a fashion designer at a fashion show. Put pictures A–D in the order that they are described.

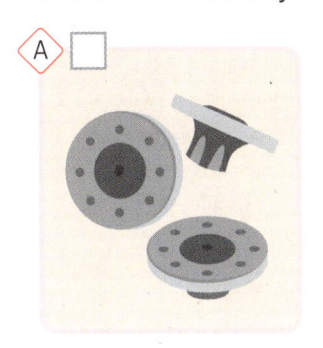

A ☐ B ☐ C ☐ D ☐

4 🔊 3.1 Listen again and choose the correct answer.
1. Dawson says that sustainable fashion aims to protect the environment and
   a recycle materials.
   b workers in the industry.
   c create fashionable clothes.
2. Sustainable fashion designers should
   a reduce the cost of production.
   b reuse materials more.
   c hire more people.
3. What is the bottom of the shoe made of?
   a material from animals
   b recycled material
   c material from a plant
4. Dawson wants people who produce cotton to
   a use recycled materials.
   b work quickly.
   c be paid well.
5. Dawson wants people to
   a think of his clothes as environmentally friendly.
   b wear his clothes in different situations.
   c do more to protect the environment.

On the Portal
Extra Practice Activities: Lesson 3.5

3.6 Speaking

Giving and responding to compliments

1 🔊 **3.2** Listen and repeat the phrases.

SPEAKING — Giving and responding to compliments

Giving compliments
You look good/great in that (outfit/colour).
It's/You're so cute/nice/friendly/kind!
Your clothes are great.   That cap's awesome.
You've got amazing hair/a nice smile.
I (really) like/love your style.   It (really) suits you.
What a cool hat!
You've got great taste in clothes.
That's really helpful/thoughtful.

Responding to compliments
Thanks.   Cheers.
You've made my day.
That's really nice of you.
Really?   Do you think so?
I'm glad you like it.

2 Decide if the sentences are giving compliments (G) or responding to compliments (R).
1 [R] You've made my day.
2 [ ] Your jewellery is great.
3 [ ] You look great in that dress.
4 [ ] I'm glad you like them.
5 [ ] Those sandals really suit you.
6 [ ] Do you think so?
7 [ ] What a cool chain!
8 [ ] Those ankle boots are awesome.

3 Complete the sentences with the words below.

| day | ~~look~~ | really | so | style | suits | taste | that |

1 You *look* great in that colour.
2 Do you think _____?
3 _____ jacket is awesome!
4 That's _____ nice of you.
5 Red really _____ you.
6 You've got great _____ in clothes.
7 You've made my _____.
8 I like your _____.

4 Choose the correct option.
1 A: I like what you're wearing today.
   B: That's really (nice) / brilliant of you.
2 A: You've got amazing hair.
   B: Thanks, you've *made / done* my day!
3 A: You've got great taste in clothes.
   B: Do you think *so / it*?
4 A: That colour really suits you.
   B: Oh, thanks. I'm *glad / awesome* you like it.
5 A: Your jacket is awesome.
   B: *Really / Very*? I don't know if I really like it.

5 🔊 **3.3** Complete the dialogue with one word in each gap. Then listen and check.

Katie: What do you think about this dress, Liz?
Liz: I love it! You ¹*look* great in that colour.
Katie: Do you ²_____ so? I'm not sure I like the pockets on the side.
Liz: I see what you mean, but it really ³_____ you, I think.
Katie: Oh, thanks, Liz. That's really nice ⁴_____ you. Oh, look at these boots – they're cute. Why don't you try them on?
Liz: OK. What do you think?
Katie: They ⁵_____ awesome! You look great ⁶_____ them.
Liz: Oh, thanks. You've got great ⁷_____ in clothes.
Katie: Thanks. You've made my ⁸_____! I love going shopping with you!

Unit 3 | 32 | I can give and respond to compliments.

On the Portal
Extra Practice Activities: Lesson 3.6

3.7 Writing
An email describing appearance

1 Decide if the adjectives are positive (P), negative (N) or neutral (NE).

_P_ attractive   ___ average   ___ brilliant
___ incredible   ___ horrible   ___ impressive
___ stunning   ___ original   ___ strange

2 Complete the adjectives in the sentences.
1. We really enjoyed the show. It was f _a_ n _t_ _a_ s _t_ _i_ _c_.
2. I'd love to be a singer, but I'm not very good, just a _ _ _ _ g _ _ .
3. Do you think it will be s _ _ _ _ n _ _ _ _ if I wear a football top to the restaurant?
4. You look s _ _ _ _ n _ _ _ _ _ in that dress!
5. That's a really o _ _ _ i _ _ _ look. I haven't seen anything like it before.
6. I hate our school uniform. It's h _ _ _ i _ _ _ !

3 Complete Stuart's email to his friend Louis with phrases a–g.
a. her outfit is similar to mine
b. I've been busy because
c. hope to see you there
d. we have cool accessories like
e. Bye for now
f. By the way
g. Thanks for your message.

✉

Subject: Come to our school play!

Hi Louis,

¹_g_ Guess what! ² ___ I've been preparing for our school play next month.
We're putting on a cool production of The Wizard of Oz. All the music in it will be hip-hop and we even have some of the latest songs in the charts! Also, ³ ___ big, gold chains and loose trousers. Sally is playing Dorothy and ⁴ ___ , but she's wearing a cap backwards.
⁵ ___ , I'm allowed to give away two free tickets to the show. I'd love it if you and Jamie could come. It'll be a lot of fun, I promise!

Anyway, ⁶ ___ .
⁷ ___ ,

Stuart

---

4 Match the sentence halves.
1. _b_ You should see Jane – she looks
2. ___ I'm looking forward to
3. ___ I've got some
4. ___ Speak
5. ___ I also wanted

a. brilliant news!
b. ~~stunning in her new dress.~~
c. to tell you about my holiday.
d. seeing you.
e. soon.

5 Complete Charlotte's notes about her school musical with the words below.

| chain   character   ~~invite~~   message   musical |
| songs   striped   to come and see |

School musical
- email Sandra to ¹_invite_ her to school musical
- thank her for her ² _____
- tell her about school ³ _____ : Mamma Mia!
- my part: Donna, Sophie's mum, the main ⁴ _____
- costume: ⁵ _____ dress, trendy shoes, ⁶ _____ and bracelets
- music: singing ABBA ⁷ _____
- ask Sandra ⁸ _____ it

WRITING TIME

6 Write Charlotte's email to Sandra.

1 Find ideas
Make notes about:
- the type of play and your character.
- your outfit and your opinion of it.
- your invitation to Sandra.

2 Plan and write
- Organise your ideas into paragraphs. Use Stuart's email in Exercise 3 to help you.
- Write a draft of your email.

3 Check
- Check language: have you used opinion adjectives to make your writing more personal?
- Check grammar: have you used the correct tenses for future events?
- Write the final version of your email.

My Language File

WORDLIST 🔊 3.4

Clothes and accessories
ankle boots (n) _____
bracelet (n) _____
cap (n) _____
chain (n) _____
elbow pads (n) _____
knee pads (n) _____
leggings (n) _____
mask (n) _____
ring (n) _____
sandals (n) _____
shoulder pads (n) _____
suit (n) _____
tights (n) _____

Adjectives to describe clothes and accessories
casual (adj) _____
checked (adj) _____
colourful (adj) _____
cotton (adj) _____
denim (adj) _____
fashionable (adj) _____
flowery (adj) _____
gold (adj) _____
leather (adj) _____
linen (adj) _____
loose (adj) _____
neat (adj) _____
old-fashioned (adj) _____
ordinary (adj) _____
plain (adj) _____
scruffy (adj) _____
silver (adj) _____
smart (adj) _____
striped (adj) _____
terrific (adj) _____
tight (adj) _____

Word friends (appearance)
be average height _____
be average size _____
be good-looking _____
be in your thirties _____
be slim _____
be well-built _____
have curly hair _____
have dark skin _____
have dyed hair _____
have freckles _____
have painted nails _____
have pale skin _____
have pierced ears _____
have straight hair _____
wear a costume _____
wear jewellery _____

Fashion
clothing rental (n) _____
ethical materials (n) _____
high street store (n) _____
individual look (n) _____
key trend (n) _____
new feature (n) _____
new outfit (n) _____
second-hand clothes (n) _____
slow fashion (n) _____
young designer (n) _____

Parts of clothes and shoes
button (n) _____
collar (n) _____
heel (n) _____
hood (n) _____
laces (n) _____
pocket (n) _____
sleeve (n) _____
sole (n) _____
zip (n) _____

Extra words
3D printed clothes (n) _____
attractive (adj) _____
average (adj) _____
awesome (adj) _____
awful (adj) _____
bright (adj) _____
brilliant (adj) _____
charity shop (n) _____
create (v) _____
design (v) _____
express your identity _____
fantastic (adj) _____
fashion choice (n) _____
fit (v) _____
go with (v) _____
helmet (n) _____
horrible (adj) _____
impressive (adj) _____
incredible (adj) _____
influencer (n) _____
item of clothing (n) _____
look (n) _____
original (adj) _____
pattern (n) _____
popular (adj) _____
scarf (n) _____
strange (adj) _____
stunning (adj) _____
style (n) _____
suit (v) _____
taste (n) _____
uncomfortable (adj) _____
uniform (n) _____

Sounds good!
I'll skip it. _____
Hang on. _____

MY LANGUAGE NOTES

My favourite words/expressions from this unit

Self-check

Vocabulary

1 Complete the sentences with the words below.

> button flowery freckles heels mask pads
> pocket sandals sleeves twenties

1 Put your keys in your coat _____ now so you won't forget them.
2 Ann wore a _____ dress to the party.
3 Don't forget your elbow and knee _____ when you go skateboarding.
4 I can't wear this shirt because a _____ has fallen off it.
5 Ana has red hair, blue eyes and _____, just like her mother.
6 It's really hot today. I think I'll wear my _____.
7 For James's birthday, we all wore a _____ which had a photo of his face on!
8 I'm not sure how old Connor is. I think he's in his _____.
9 The _____ on this top are too long – they go over my hands, look!
10 I prefer shoes with high _____ because they make me look taller!

2 Match words 1–10 with definitions a–j

1 ☐ plain
2 ☐ stunning
3 ☐ dyed
4 ☐ pale
5 ☐ ring
6 ☐ scruffy
7 ☐ checked
8 ☐ tight
9 ☐ average height
10 ☐ incredible

a not its natural colour
b fitting your body very closely
c jewellery you wear on your finger
d not having any pattern
e very light in colour
f very beautiful
g not tall or short
h having a pattern with squares
i dirty and untidy
j so good that it's difficult to believe

Grammar

3 Complete the sentences with the Present Perfect Continuous form of the verbs in brackets or *for*, *since* and *all*.

1 I _____ (work) hard on it since June.
2 Sally _____ (study) since 6 a.m.
3 It has been raining _____ day.
4 We _____ (not wait) for very long.
5 The neighbours have been making lots of noise _____ hours now!
6 My brother hasn't been writing his blog much _____ last month.
7 I've been calling you _____ morning!

4 Complete the text with the Present Perfect Simple or Present Perfect Continuous form of the verbs in brackets.

Clothes and memories

I ¹_____ (tidy) my wardrobe and I ²_____ (find) a lot of clothes which have important memories for me. For example, a T-shirt which I ³_____ (have) for five years. I ⁴_____ (grow) a lot since then, so it doesn't fit any more, but I bought it in Italy one year. I ⁵_____ (think) about that trip a lot since then, because it was a great time. I ⁶_____ (find) an old blanket too. I must stop now, though, because I ⁷_____ (do) this all afternoon and I ⁸_____ (not finish) my homework yet!

Speaking

5 Complete the dialogues with one word in each gap.

1 A: That T-shirt is awesome!
   B: Do you _____ so? I'm not sure I like it.
2 A: I like your style.
   B: Thanks, that's really nice _____ you.
3 A: Those leggings really _____ you.
   B: Thanks!
4 A: You've got great taste in clothes.
   B: Thanks. You've made my _____!
5 A: You _____ great in that colour.
   B: Cheers.

YOUR SCORE

Vocabulary: __/20   Speaking: __/5
Grammar: __/15   Total: __/40

Reading Time 1

Hanae Mori

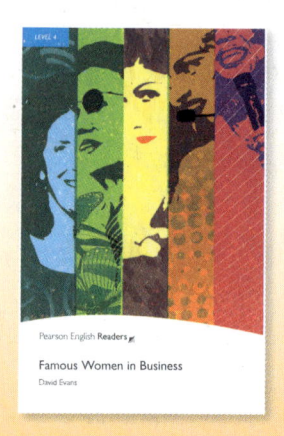

As she grew up, Hanae often argued with her father about her future. He wanted her to be like him and to become a doctor, but Hanae wanted to study art.

'Art?' her father used to say. 'Art is a wonderful hobby, but it's not a real subject to study.'

In the end they agreed that Hanae would study literature, and so she left her family and started a course in Japanese Literature at university in Tokyo. But before she could finish her studies, the Second World War started. Like many other women students, Hanae had to stop studying and go to work in a factory. Soon she realised that the war was going badly for Japan. Every night she heard the American planes above Tokyo and she listened for the sound of the explosions as the bombs fell on the city around her.

When the war ended in 1945, Japan had a lot of problems. Many of its cities had been destroyed, and millions of its people had been killed. But Hanae wanted to return to normal as quickly as possible. So she went back to university and finished her studies in 1947. At that time there seemed little chance that she would go into business.

The year before, Hanae had fallen in love with a rich young man called Ken Mori, whose family owned a factory that made cloth. They were soon married and it seemed that Hanae would become a housewife. Until the end of the Second World War, Japan had been a very traditional society and a woman was simply expected to be a good wife and a wise mother. At first, Hanae was ready to accept this situation.

'I had no problem with becoming a housewife,' she said. But it was soon clear that a life at home, looking after her husband and her family, was not for her. After just a few months, Hanae was bored. She started looking around for something to keep her busy.

In the late 1940s, Japanese society was slowly changing. In 1946, Japanese women had been allowed to vote for the first time and a few women had become politicians in Japan's parliament. There were still very few Japanese businesswomen, but if women could become politicians, why couldn't they also become successful in other areas? Hanae decided to try business.

She had always been interested in clothes, she loved art and she was married to a man who owned a cloth factory. So the clothes business was the obvious choice for her. Over the next two years, she learnt about designing clothes, cutting cloth, selling clothes and running a business. By 1951, she felt that she was ready to make and sell her own clothes. She started in a small way, making clothes for a few people, but then she had a piece of luck. An important Japanese film producer saw one of her designs and loved it. He called Hanae.

'Could you make some clothes for my next film?' he asked. Hanae said 'yes' without even thinking about it.

Hanae Mori

Before you read

1 Complete the sentences with the correct form of the phrases below.

> argue with   have a piece of luck   return to normal
> run a business   seem little chance

1 I always _____ my brother about what video games we're going to play.
2 After the crisis, it took a long time for things to _____.
3 With the home team losing by three goals, there _____ that they would win.
4 James _____ on the way home. He found ten euros!
5 Your grandad _____ successfully for many years before he retired.

While you read

2 🔊 RT1.1 Read and listen to the story. Put events a–h in the order they happen.

a ☐ She worked in a factory.
b ☐ She became bored with being a housewife.
c ☐ She discussed what she wanted to study with her father.
d ☐ A film producer called her.
e ☐ She met Ken Mori.
f ☐ She finished university.
g ☐ She started university.
h ☐ She started selling her own clothes.

3 Mark the sentences T (true) or F (false).

1 ☐ Hanae's father agreed to her studying Art at university.
2 ☐ Lots of bombs fell on Tokyo during the war.
3 ☐ Hanae went into business immediately after finishing university.
4 ☐ Her husband was wealthy.
5 ☐ At first, Hanae was happy to be a housewife.
6 ☐ The first clothes she made were for a famous film director.

After you read

4 Match the highlighted phrases in the story with the definitions.

1 take up her time: _____
2 do well in something: _____
3 start a company: _____
4 was the best option: _____
5 the opposite of 'going well': _____

5 Look at the adjectives below from the story and complete the text with them. There is one extra adjective.

> bored   real   successful   traditional
> wonderful   young

In ^{1}_____ Japanese society, women weren't encouraged to work – their main responsibility was to look after the family. However, some women felt ^{2}_____ sitting at home. They wanted to work and be independent, and felt they had ^{3}_____ skills they could offer to society. So, after the Second World War, more and more women started to work and became ^{4}_____ in business. Things change, and this was a ^{5}_____ thing for some Japanese women, like Hanae Mori.

6 WRAP UP Complete the information about the story.

Title: _____
Type: *love story / biography / adventure story*
Main characters: _____
_____
Important object: _____
My opinion: ☆☆☆☆☆

37 Unit 3

Work hard, dream big!

VOCABULARY
Jobs | Work | Working conditions | Job training | Success at work

GRAMMAR
Talking about the future | Future Continuous

4.1 Vocabulary

Work and jobs

1 ● Look at the photos and complete the words for jobs.

1 p*lumber*
2 m_____
3 p_____ t_____
4 c_____
5 f_____ a_____
6 i_____
7 l_____
8 s_____ a_____
9 f_____ d_____

2 ●● Match the descriptions with the jobs below.

app developer   blogger   engineer   fashion designer
freelance journalist   interpreter   lab assistant
music critic   psychologist   ~~travel agent~~

I organise people's summer holidays for them.
1 *travel agent*

I write posts online about my experiences.
2 _____

I design and create trendy new clothes.
3 _____

I write games and programs for mobile phones.
4 _____

I write articles for different newspapers and news websites.
5 _____

I listen to a lot of new music and write reviews.
6 _____

I help my boss at work – she's a scientist.
7 _____

I design and build roads and bridges.
8 _____

I help people with their mental health.
9 _____

I translate what people are saying in real time.
10 _____

3 **WORD FRIENDS** Match the sentence halves.
1. [d] I'd like to do
2. [ ] Have you heard about Jack? He got
3. [ ] It's great to be part
4. [ ] Before you start looking for jobs, you need to write
5. [ ] Successful app developers can earn a
6. [ ] My uncle isn't working at the moment. He's

a. of a team in my job. I learn a lot from my colleagues.
b. good salary.
c. a CV.
d. ~~some voluntary work this summer.~~
e. fired for being rude to a customer!
f. unemployed.

4 Choose the correct option.

My brother's new job

When my brother finished university, the first thing he did was ¹(write)/ make his CV. One day he saw an advert for a job he liked, so he decided to ² look / apply for it. The company liked his CV and they asked him to come in and ³ meet / have an interview. A week later, they phoned him and told him he was successful. They asked him to come back the next day to ⁴ get / sign a contract and ⁵ meet / give his colleagues. He's been there a week now and really enjoys it. They said that if he works hard, he'll ⁶ apply for / get a promotion!

5 Choose the correct answer.
1. My boss told me that I'm going to get a pay ___ next month!
   a. up   b. rate   (c.) rise
2. My cousin has a really ___-paid job in the city.
   a. good   b. well   c. hourly
3. We have flexible working ___ here, so you can choose when to start in the morning.
   a. overtime   b. hours   c. holidays
4. If you have any questions, just ask any member of ___.
   a. staff   b. colleagues   c. job
5. We can offer a good hourly ___ to the right person.
   a. pay   b. rate   c. price
6. In this job, you'll get four weeks' paid ___ a year.
   a. holiday   b. bonus   c. hours

6 Complete the sentences with the words below. There are three extra words.

contract	~~electrician~~	flexible	flight	freelance
has	overtime	programmer	quit	rate
temporary	time	trainer		

1. My dad loves his job as an *electrician*, and the hourly _____ is good too.
2. My sister's just started working as a computer _____ in a tech company. She's on a trial _____ at the moment, but she's hoping to get a permanent _____ soon.
3. Judy _____ her job last year to become a _____ journalist.
4. My mum is a _____ attendant and she has to work a lot of _____. Sometimes I don't see her for three days!
5. My friend _____ an interview tomorrow for a job as a personal _____.

7 Complete the words in the text.

Living your dreams

My cousin works as a computer ¹p*rogrammer* in a big company. It's a ²w_____-p_____ job and he ³e_____ a good salary. He has ⁴f_____ working hours, so he can choose what time to start work each day. There are also quite generous ⁵p_____ holidays. He works hard and recently he got a ⁶p_____. He got a bigger office and a big pay ⁷r_____, but now he has to work lots of ⁸o_____ – sometimes he doesn't finish work till 9 p.m.

He says he isn't happy, though, and is thinking about giving ⁹u_____ this job. He wants to work in the music industry – he's always dreamed of becoming a music ¹⁰c_____. He's determined to follow his dream. He even joked once that he wants to get ¹¹f_____ so he can go and apply ¹²f_____ the job of his dreams!

I can talk about jobs and work.

4.2 Grammar
Talking about the future

GRAMMAR — Talking about the future

will
I'**ll send** you a photo. (spontaneous decision)
I **won't miss** the British weather. (prediction)

be going to
I'**m going to work** there. (plan)
It'**s going to be** great. (prediction based on facts)

Present Continuous
My uncle **is starting** a new business this summer. (arrangement)

Present Simple
My flight **leaves** the day after we finish school. (schedule)

Look at the future forms of *can* and *must*.
I **can** go swimming. → I'**ll be able to** go swimming.
You **must** come and visit me. → You'**ll have to** come and visit me.

1 ● Choose the correct option.
1. Naomi was rude to several customers and she (**'s going to get**) / **will get** fired from her job at the café!
2. We need to hurry – the lesson **starts** / **will start** in ten minutes.
3. I don't know how to prepare for the job interview. **Will** / **Do** you help me?
4. I **will meet** / **'m meeting** my friends for lunch at 1 p.m. tomorrow.
5. I **look** / **'m going to look** for a part-time job next month.

2 ●● Complete the text messages with the correct future form of the verbs in brackets.

1. Did you remember to buy milk?
   Oh no, sorry! I'**ll get** (get) some on the way home. 😊

2. What are you up to this weekend?
   I _____ (meet) Louis and Amelia for a pizza on Saturday evening. Want to come?

3. Jane had an interview for a summer job today, didn't she?
   Yes, and I think she _____ (get) the job. It sounds perfect for her.

3 ●●● Choose the correct answer.

Leo: Have you got any plans for the summer, Ava?
Ava: Not really. I think I [1]___ at home. What about you?
Leo: I [2]___ a summer job – it's all arranged.
Ava: Wow, really? What [3]___ do?
Leo: Well, I [4]___ at the publishing company my aunt works for – she's an editor there. I can choose whether I want to work in the office or have training as a journalist.
Ava: And what [5]___?
Leo: I [6]___ as a journalist. I think it [7]___ more interesting than office work.
Ava: Definitely! That sounds great, Leo. I'm jealous! You [8]___ tell me all about it when you're there.
Leo: Of course! I [9]___ you on the first day to let you know how I'm getting on.
Ava: Please do. Oh, is that the time? I should go. My train [10]___ in three minutes! See you!
Leo: Bye, Ava. Speak soon!

1. (a) 'll just relax   b 'm just relaxing   c just relax
2. a 'm getting   b 'll get   c get
3. a do you   b will you   c are you going to
4. a work   b 'm going to work   c 'll work
5. a you are doing   b do you do   c are you going to do
6. a 'm going to train   b 'll train   c train
7. a is being   b be   c will be
8. a 'll must   b 'll have to   c 're having to
9. a 'm texting   b 'll text   c 'm going to text
10. a leaves   b will leave   c can leave

I can use different tenses to talk about future events.

On the Portal
Extra Practice Activities: Lesson 4.2

4.3 Reading and Vocabulary
Unusual jobs

1 Complete the sentences with a word from box A and a word/phrase from box B.

A | be ~~gain~~ get (x2) practical professional training (x2) virtual

B | a specialist an opportunity course experience feedback skills training ~~work experience~~ workshop

1 My cousin worked at a bank during her university holidays, so she could *gain work experience* in the industry.
2 How often do you _____ from your boss about how well you work?
3 My dad's company send him away to do a two-week _____ every six months.
4 At school, we sometimes _____ to meet people who work in different jobs and ask them questions about their work.
5 Regular training is important in order to improve employees' _____.
6 Don't forget we have to take part in a _____ next Tuesday on improving sales techniques.
7 You don't need to come to the centre, as we provide _____ online.
8 Students spend six weeks working in an engineering company to give them _____.
9 Ava is a qualified doctor, but she's training to _____ in neurology.

2 Read the article quickly and choose the best title.
a Working in sport
b Emerging careers
c The robots are coming!

3 Read the article again and answer the questions.
1 What will an e-sports coach help their team to do?
2 What two things will you need as an e-sports coach?
3 What will companies use drones for?
4 What job does the article compare a drone manager to?
5 Who will a talker work with?
6 What technology will a talker use?

I can understand an article about unusual jobs.

In the coming years, it is expected that a lot of the jobs we do will be replaced by Artificial Intelligence (AI) and robots. This means that more people are going to be looking for new jobs and new ways of working, and will need to develop professional skills in new areas. Here, we take a look at three of the new jobs that some people will want to do.

1 E-sports coach
E-sports, or electronic sports, are becoming more and more popular as people play video games competitively in tournaments. Like traditional sports teams, e-sports teams need training. As an e-sports coach, employed by a team, you will help your trainees win tournaments. This will involve recording games, then watching them back and analysing the team's skills and weaknesses so they can improve. You won't need any formal qualifications, but you'll need understanding and skill in the particular game you're working with.

2 Drone manager
The use of drones is going to increase in the near future. This won't be just for recreation, but also as more companies begin to use them for deliveries. This means the skies are going to get busy, and all these drones in the sky will need careful management. As a drone manager, you'll do similar work to an air traffic controller at an airport, but for drones. You'll need to be a specialist not just in flying a drone, but also in communication between organisations and customers.

3 Talker
The world's population is getting older, and some elderly people may feel lonely. At the same time, younger people will have to look for new types of work. The job of talker aims to solve both of these problems. As a talker, you'll be connected to a platform and will have flexible working hours. You'll just sign on and off when you can. Your job will be to have conversations with people who are lonely, using a special app and headphones. The most important skill you'll need is to be able to listen to people.

4.4 Grammar
Future Continuous

GRAMMAR Future Continuous

I'll be speaking with a Scottish accent.
I won't be living in Bedford.
What will you be doing?
Will you be working? Yes, I will./No, I won't.

Time expressions
this time next month/year, this/next weekend/week, in five years/in five years' time, at 9 p.m. tonight, in the future

1 ● Match the sentence halves.

1. [c] At 6 p.m. tonight, I'll
2. [ ] When will
3. [ ] Harry and Andrew won't be
4. [ ] In twenty
5. [ ] Next summer, Anya
6. [ ] What will you be

a years, I'll be working for a big company.
b doing at 10 p.m. tonight?
c ~~be having dinner with my family.~~
d will be working at a summer camp.
e Liz be having her interview?
f working here next year.

2 ● Complete the post and comments with the Future Continuous form of the verbs in brackets.

Shirley Thomas
Yay! The exams are finally over and this time next week, I ¹*'ll be working* (work) in an animal shelter. What about you? What ² _____ (you/do) this summer?

Graeme Marks In two weeks, I ³ _____ (start) a summer job at the beach.

Julia Somme We ⁴ _____ (not go) abroad on holiday. 😭

Ritchie Alba I ⁵ _____ (stay) in Greece with my cousin!

Gemma Sykes That sounds cool, Shirley! ⁶ _____ (you/write) about the shelter on your blog?

Shirley Thomas Of course! And I ⁷ _____ (post) lots of photos of our animals too!

3 ●● Complete the sentences with one word in each gap.

1. I hope I'll be working with animals *in* the future.
2. Will you _____ seeing Alice tonight?
3. What will you be doing _____ 10 a.m. tomorrow?
4. They _____ be studying Italian next year because they won't have time.
5. This is my last year at this school. _____ year, I'll be starting a new school.
6. In twenty years, I hope I'll be _____ an interesting job.

4 ●●● Complete the blog post with the Future Continuous form of the verbs below. There are two extra verbs.

| apply | design | earn | gain | have | show | start |
| ~~study~~ | relax | work | | | | |

How I'll get my dream job
I love technology and my dream is to become an app developer. These are the things I think I'll be doing at different times to achieve this dream.

1. This year, I *will be studying* for my exams.
2. In two years, I _____ for university.
3. While I'm at university, I _____ my own apps.
4. In five years, I _____ job interviews.
5. In ten years, I _____ lots of experience in a tech company.
6. In fifteen years, I _____ my own company.
7. In twenty years, I _____ lots of money.
8. I'll retire early, and in thirty years, I _____ on a beach!

What about you? What's your dream job?

Unit 4 — 42 — I can use the Future Continuous to talk about actions in progress in the future.

On the Portal
Extra Practice Activities: Lesson 4.4

4.5 Listening and Vocabulary
Success at work

1 Use the clues to complete the crossword.

```
        1
        e
    2   m
    c   p
      3 l
      s o
  4 d   y
        e
5 a     r
      6 c
```

Across

4 At the end of the course, you'll receive a _____.
5 My sister has won an _____ for her school project.
6 When I graduate, I'd like to start a successful _____ as a doctor.

Down

1 This *employer* pays its staff well and gives them five weeks' paid holiday a year.
2 There were ten _____ at the job interview, but only one was successful.
3 Our boss began his _____ by describing his plans for the coming year.

2 🔊 4.1 Listen to Harry and Maisie talking about their future. Who wants to start their own business?

_____

3 🔊 4.1 Listen again and choose the correct answer.

1 What is Maisie going to do when she's older?
   a She's going to work with children.
   b She's going to work with animals.
   c She's not sure.
2 What does Maisie NOT talk about?
   a earning money
   b having paid holidays
   c doing something interesting
3 What's important to Harry?
   a holidays
   b working in a team
   c a good salary
4 Who does Harry work for?
   a himself
   b a pet shop
   c a local newspaper
5 What's the first thing he wants to do when he finishes school?
   a start a company
   b study Business
   c work hard
6 What does Maisie NOT say is important?
   a studying
   b family
   c health

4 Complete sentences 1–5 from the listening with the words below. Then match the phrases in bold in the sentences with meanings a–e below.

| billionaire | bothered | happens | impressed | ~~no~~ |

1 **I have *no* idea**!
2 **I'm not that** _____ about earning a huge salary.
3 **As it** _____, I already have my own business.
4 **I'm really** _____, Harry.
5 I think you'll **become a** _____ when you're older.

a ☐ actually
b ☐ have over £1,000,000,000
c [1] I really don't know
d ☐ I respect and admire what you've done
e ☐ this is not important to me

I can understand a conversation about success at work.

4.6 Speaking
Warnings, recommendations and prohibition

1 🔊 **4.2** Listen and repeat the phrases.

> **SPEAKING** — Warnings, recommendations and prohibition
>
> **Warning**
> Pay attention!   Mind your head!
> Look out!   Watch out!   Be careful (you don't hurt yourself).
> If you're not careful, you'll hit your head.
>
> **Recommending**
> Remember to lock the door.   Don't forget to lock the door.
> Make sure you (don't) let it get hot.
> Be sure to wear the right colours.   Be sure not to be late.
>
> **Prohibiting**
> Whatever you do, don't drop it!
> You can't/mustn't leave too early.
> You're not allowed to leave too early.

2 Match the sentence halves.

1. [b] Make sure
2. [ ] Pay
3. [ ] Whatever you
4. [ ] You're not
5. [ ] If you're not careful,
6. [ ] Mind your

a do, don't leave the window open.
b ~~you don't spill any of this liquid.~~
c allowed to wear white shoes to work.
d head when you go through that door!
e you'll hurt yourself.
f attention! This is important.

3 Complete the dialogues with the words below.

> forget   ~~look~~   out   remember   sure

1. A: Can I speak to you for a …
   B: *Look* out! There's a car coming!
2. A: Don't _____ to feed the cat while we're away.
   B: Don't worry, of course I won't.
3. A: Watch _____!
   B: Oh thanks! That nearly fell on me.
4. A: And then I put this plate in here, right?
   B: Yes, but be _____ to use gloves to lift it. It's really hot.
5. A: Is that everything?
   B: Almost. _____ to lock up everything at the end of the day.

4 🔊 **4.3** Complete the dialogue with one word in each gap. Then listen and check.

Mia: Hi, Ian. Nice to meet you. I'm Mia – I'm your manager. Let's get started then. Follow me through to the back. Mind your ¹*head* – that's really low! This is your locker and key. Don't ² _____ to lock it every time you leave work. I see you're wearing a black shirt. That's great – it's what we all wear here. Make ³ _____ you wear black shoes too. You're not ⁴ _____ to wear other colours.

Ian: OK.

Mia: Right, so this is the coffee machine. Watch ⁵ _____ – it's hot! Now, please ⁶ _____ attention and don't touch anything until I've shown it to you, OK? If you're not ⁷ _____, you'll burn yourself on it.

Ian: Oh, sorry.

Mia: So, when it's making coffee, remember ⁸ _____ keep an eye on it. And don't let it get too hot. You can change the temperature here.

Ian: OK, what temperature should it be?

Mia: Well, whatever you ⁹ _____, don't let it go over 120 degrees.

Ian: Got it.

Mia: OK, so next let's look at the sandwich toaster …

Unit 4   44   I can give warnings, make recommendations and express prohibition.

On the Portal
Extra Practice Activities: Lesson 4.6

4.7 Writing
A job application letter

1 Complete the letter with the words below.

> addition   applying   available   currently   forward
> gain   regarding   ~~response~~   taking

Dear Sir/Madam,

I am writing in ¹*response* to your advertisement. I am interested in ² _____ for the post of social programme assistant at your summer school in Bournemouth. I am ³ _____ in my final year at high school and I hope to study Physical Education at university. Therefore, I am very keen to ⁴ _____ work experience.

⁵ _____ the post, I play a lot of sports and I have done swimming coaching at my local leisure centre. In ⁶ _____, I have a National Pool Lifeguard Qualification. Furthermore, I am based in Bournemouth, so I am familiar with local attractions and events. I am a very social person and I love meeting overseas students from different cultures.

Thank you for ⁷ _____ the time to read my application. I am ⁸ _____ for an interview at any time.

I look ⁹ _____ to hearing from you.

Yours faithfully,
Alice Morgan

2 Match informal phrases 1–8 with formal phrases with similar meanings a–h.

1. [c] Hi there,
2. [ ] I'm really into meeting people.
3. [ ] Speak soon.
4. [ ] You can interview me now.
5. [ ] Get in touch when you want.
6. [ ] I saw your job ad.
7. [ ] About the job,
8. [ ] I really want the job.

a I look forward to hearing from you.
b I am currently available for an interview.
c ~~Dear Sir/Madam,~~
d I am writing in response to your job advertisement.
e Regarding the position,
f I am very interested in the post.
g I am a very social person.
h Please do not hesitate to contact me.

3 Choose one of the jobs in these adverts. Make notes to answer the questions below.

Data clerk
Do you want experience working in a bank this summer?
We are looking for junior data clerks to work in the month of July. You will be good at Maths and have experience of using spreadsheets.
Please apply to Tom Sharp,
HR Department, Exeter Bank.

Receptionist
We are looking for a person to work on our reception desk at a residential home for the elderly this summer. You will have good interpersonal skills and an interest in helping people.

Please apply to **Ruth Mayors** at the address below.

Job application notes
1 *Reason for writing*
_____
2 *What are you doing now?*
_____
3 *Describe your experience*
_____
4 *Describe your personal qualities*
_____

WRITING TIME

4 Write a job application letter for the advert you chose in Exercise 3.

1 Find ideas
Make notes about:
- your reasons for wanting the job.
- what you are doing now.
- your experience and personal qualities.

2 Plan and write
- Organise your ideas into paragraphs. Use Alice's letter in Exercise 1 to help you.
- Write a draft of your letter.

3 Check
- Check language: have you used a formal style?
- Check grammar: have you used future tenses correctly?
- Write the final version of your letter.

I can write a job application letter.

My Language File

WORDLIST 🔊 4.4

Jobs
accountant (n) _____
blogger (n) _____
cleaner (n) _____
electrician (n) _____
engineer (n) _____
influencer (n) _____
interpreter (n) _____
librarian (n) _____
mechanic (n) _____
plumber (n) _____
psychologist (n) _____
translator (n) _____

Jobs: compound nouns
app developer (n) _____
computer programmer (n) _____
fashion designer (n) _____
film director (n) _____
flight attendant (n) _____
freelance journalist (n) _____
lab assistant (n) _____
music critic (n) _____
personal trainer (n) _____
shop assistant (n) _____
travel agent (n) _____

Word friends (work)
apply for a job _____
be part of a team _____
be unemployed _____
do voluntary work _____
earn a salary _____
earn a wage _____
feel part of a team _____
get a promotion _____
get fired _____
give up a job _____
have an interview _____
meet your colleagues _____
quit a job _____
send off a CV _____
sign a contract _____
write a CV _____

Working conditions
badly-paid (adj) _____
do overtime _____
flexible working hours (n) _____
hourly rate (n) _____
member of staff (n) _____
paid holidays (n) _____
pay rise (n) _____
permanent contract (n) _____
temporary contract (n) _____
well-paid (adj) _____
work overtime _____

Job training
do a training course _____
gain work experience _____
get an opportunity to _____
get feedback from _____
give practical experience _____
improve professional skills _____
provide virtual training _____
take part in a training workshop _____
train to be a specialist _____

Success at work
award (n) _____
candidate (n) _____
career (n) _____
diploma (n) _____
employer (n) _____
speech (n) _____

Extra words
agency (n) _____
application (n) _____
charity shop (n) _____
complete a course _____
concentrate (v) _____
construction worker (n) _____
deal with customers _____
do housework _____
earn a fortune _____
efficient (adj) _____
fall behind (v) _____
make a career of something _____
management (n) _____
newsreader (n) _____
part-time position _____
personal qualities (n) _____
profession (n) _____
put money into something _____
qualification (n) _____
qualified (adj) _____
receptionist (n) _____
surgeon (n) _____
take time off _____
train for a job _____
trainee (n) _____
vacancy (n) _____
work as a team _____
work from home _____
work independently _____
workplace accident (n) _____

Sounds good!
Keep an eye on it. _____
Good luck! _____
You did a great job. _____

MY LANGUAGE NOTES

My favourite words/expressions from this unit

Self-check

Vocabulary

1 Choose the correct option.
1 James is a *psychologist / librarian* and he helps people with their mental health.
2 The *cleaner / accountant* usually starts work after everybody has left for the day.
3 My mum works as a *lab assistant / travel agent*, so we get cheap holidays!
4 The *mechanic / electrician* was terrible – our car doesn't even start now!
5 Carla is a *fashion designer / shop assistant*. She creates beautiful clothes.
6 Did you know that Tom's dad is a famous social media *influencer / plumber*?
7 I'd love to be a *personal trainer / film director* and make movies.
8 Working as an *interpreter / translator* is stressful. You have to translate speech in real time.

2 Match the words below with the definitions.

> flexible working hours   member of staff   pay rise
> salary   temporary contract   well-paid

1 when you can choose what time to start/finish work: _____
2 a regular payment you receive for working: _____
3 a job where you receive a lot of money is this: _____
4 when the money you get from a job increases: _____
5 a job with this is for a fixed/short period of time: _____
6 one of the people who work somewhere: _____

3 Complete the words in the sentences.
1 You should follow a c_____ in teaching. You'd be very good at it.
2 Pam is a professional b_____. She describes different products on her website.
3 The shoe factory is the largest e_____ in this area.
4 Chiara's a successful fashion designer and she's won several a_____ for her work.
5 I'm really nervous. I have an i_____ for a job I really want to get tomorrow.

Grammar

4 Complete the dialogues with the correct future form of the verbs in brackets.
1 A: What are your plans for this evening?
   B: I _____ (watch) the last episode of that drama.
2 A: I'm really hungry after that football match.
   B: I _____ (make) you a sandwich if you like.
3 A: Do you think Macy _____ (pass) the exam?
   B: I'm not sure. She hasn't studied much at all.
4 A: What time do we need to leave?
   B: Our train _____ (leave) at ten, so hurry up.
5 A: Oh no! Look at those dark clouds.
   B: You're right. It _____ (rain).
6 A: What _____ (you/do) tomorrow? Any plans?
   B: No, I'm not sure yet.
7 A: How are we getting there in the morning?
   B: By bus. It _____ (stop) outside the shop at 7.
8 A: Any plans for the weekend?
   B: No, I'm tired. I _____ (stay) at home.

5 Complete the text with the Future Continuous form of the verbs below. There is one extra verb.

> apply   choose   go   live   move   not do   study   work

This time next year ¹_____ in New York! My mum has been promoted. She ²_____ at the same company, but she ³_____ the same job. We ⁴_____ there at the end of the year. I ⁵_____ to a new school. In a few years' time, I ⁶_____ to universities there too. Hopefully, I ⁷_____ somewhere really good. I'm really excited!

Speaking

6 Choose the correct option.
1 A: Look *out / after*! You nearly hit me!
   B: Oh dear, sorry!
2 A: You're not allowed *of sitting / to sit* here.
   B: Oh right, sorry. I didn't know that.
3 A: Be sure *listen / to listen* to the customer.
   B: OK, I will.
4 A: Don't forget *to feed / feeding* the cat. *Do / Make* sure she has water in a bowl.
   B: No problem.

YOUR SCORE

Vocabulary: __/20   Speaking: __/5
Grammar: __/15   Total: __/40

To the stars and beyond

VOCABULARY
Space | Dimensions and distance | Large numbers | Space travel | Space science

GRAMMAR
Zero, First and Second Conditionals | Third Conditional

5 5.1 Vocabulary

Space

1 ● Look at the photos and complete the words.

1 c*omet*
2 a_____ 
3 the International S_____ S_____ 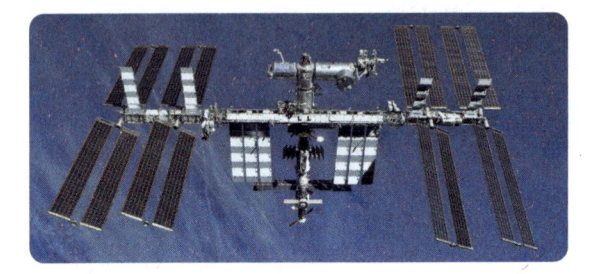
4 s_____ 
5 p_____ 
6 E_____ 
7 o_____ 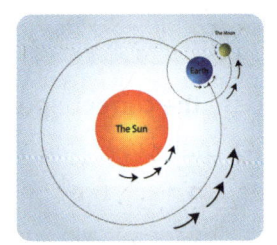
8 m_____ 
9 t_____ 

2 ●● Write the correct word for each definition.

1 a scientist who studies the stars and planets: a*stronome*r
2 a device which uses mirrors to make distant objects look larger and closer: t_____e
3 a man-made object moving around a planet in space – it can send digital information across the world: s_____e
4 a person who travels in space: a_____t
5 the collection of eight planets (including Earth) and their moons that travel around the Sun: s_____r s_____m
6 a system of millions or billions of stars – ours is called the Milky Way: g_____y

3 ● **WORD FRIENDS** Decide if the pairs of sentences are the same (S) or different (D).

1 It's 120 cm long.
The length is 120 cm. *S*
2 We're ten kilometres away from home.
We're travelling at ten kilometres an hour. ____
3 The mountain is 3,000 m high.
The width of the mountain is 3,000 m. ____
4 I live five kilometres from school.
My school is five kilometres away. ____
5 The speed limit is thirty kilometres per hour.
The speed limit is thirty kilometres an hour. ____
6 It takes me twenty minutes to get home from here.
My journey home is twenty kilometres long. ____

Unit 5 48

4 ●● Complete the sentences with one word in each gap.

1 The satellite is ten metres *long*.
2 The _____ is ten metres.
3 It's four metres _____.
4 The _____ is four metres. 
5 Slow down! You're doing 120 kilometres per _____! 
6 I live twelve kilometres _____ my school.
7 It usually _____ me thirty-five minutes to cycle there.

5 ● Write the numbers.

1 six hundred and fifty-eight: *658*
2 eight million three hundred thousand: _____
3 three thousand seven hundred and sixty-nine: _____
4 four billion eight hundred and seventy-two thousand: _____
5 nine point three million: _____

6 ●● Choose the correct option.

1 The number of (satellites) / telescopes in the Earth's orbit at the moment is estimated to be four *thousand / thousands* five hundred and fifty.
2 Our *galaxy / moon* is over a *hundred, thousand / hundred thousand* light years across.
3 The satellite is twenty metres *long / length* and its *wide / width* is five metres.
4 The closest *star / spacecraft* to our Sun is *four point two / four stop two* light years away.
5 There are normally six or seven *astronomers / astronauts* on board the space *station / system*, but sometimes there are ten or more.
6 The railway station is ten kilometres *from / away* the city centre. It *takes / walks* half an hour to get there.
7 There are eight *planets / stars* in our *space station / solar system*.
8 If you look carefully through the *satellite / telescope*, you can sometimes see a *comet / moon*.

7 ●● Write the numbers as words.

1 6,499: *six thousand four hundred and ninety-nine*
2 6.8 billion: _____
3 7,000,300,000: _____
4 123: _____
5 476,000: _____
6 12,413,389,672: _____

8 ●●● Complete the words in the article.

Space facts
you might not know

The closest ¹p*lanet* to Earth is Venus, which is over about sixty-one million kilometres ²a_____. The furthest planet from Earth in our solar ³s_____ is Neptune, which is up to 4.6 billion kilometres ⁴f_____ Earth. Some think that Pluto is the furthest at 7.47 billion kilometres away, but in 2006 scientists decided that Pluto is not actually a planet. The largest planet is Jupiter, and it has at least sixty-seven ⁵m_____ in its orbit.

The first ⁶a_____ was Yuri Gagarin. He travelled into ⁷o_____ on Vostok 1 and in 1961 became the first man in space. Vostok 1 was small – it was only 2.3 metres ⁸w_____ – and the mission lasted a hundred ⁹a_____ eight minutes. This was incredible at the time because a spacecraft has to travel at over 40,000 kilometres ¹⁰p_____ hour to leave the Earth's atmosphere.

I can talk about space and use large numbers.

5.2 Grammar
Zero, First and Second Conditionals

GRAMMAR — Zero, First and Second Conditionals

Zero Conditional: things that are always true
if/when/unless + Present Simple, Present Simple/imperative
When they complete the training, they are able to go to Mars.

First Conditional: possible situations in the future
if/unless + Present Simple, will + infinitive/imperative
If her dreams come true, she'll travel to Mars!

Second Conditional: unlikely or imaginary situations
if/unless + Past Simple, would + infinitive (without to)
What would life be like if you were an astronaut?

1 ● Choose the correct option.
1. If the rocket (launches) / launched at the right time, it will reach the moon in six weeks.
2. You won't see the comet *unless / if* you have a good telescope.
3. I always watch *Star Watch* if *it's / it will be* on TV.
4. I wouldn't go into space if you *pay / paid* me!
5. Would you study Astronomy if you *have / had* the chance?
6. If the weather isn't good, you *won't / will* see the planet clearly.

2 ●● Complete the sentences with the words below.

| doesn't | don't | gets | ~~had~~ (x2) | switch |
| will | won't | would (x2) | | |

1. If I *had* enough money, I _____ buy a telescope.
2. If it _____ rain tonight, we _____ see the moon.
3. I _____ travel more if I _____ more time.
4. If the computer _____ too hot, _____ it off.
5. My parents _____ be happy if I _____ pass my exams.

3 ●● Choose the correct option.

Interviewer: Good afternoon, Colin. How are the preparations for the next mission going?
Colin: Very well, thanks. If the weather ¹(is)/ *was* good, we'll leave Earth on Friday. Then, if everything goes well, we ² *reach / will reach* the space station in two days.
Interviewer: Could anything go wrong?
Colin: Of course. For example, the weather might be bad. If that happened, we ³ *will / would* wait until it got better. Also, if any of the rocket's systems ⁴ *fail / failed*, we would use the emergency spacecraft to return to Earth.
Interviewer: Well, let's hope everything goes well. What do people need to do if they ⁵ *want / will want* to see the space station from Earth?
Colin: Well, you ⁶ *don't / won't* see the space station unless you have a good telescope. If you want to know when it passes over your area, ⁷ *check / checked* on our website.
Interviewer: Thanks very much, Colin, and good luck!

4 ●● Complete the text with the correct form of the verbs in brackets.

Build your own telescope

If you ¹ *want* (want) to see the stars and planets, you need a good quality telescope. Unfortunately, they aren't cheap. In fact, if you ² _____ (want) to buy a really good one, you'd need to have a lot of money. But don't worry. If you really want to look at the stars, you ³ _____ (can) make your own telescope.

All you need is a cardboard tube – the ones you ⁴ _____ (use) if you want to send a poster by mail – and a couple of lenses. Make sure you cut the tube very straight. This is important as you ⁵ _____ (not be able) to change the focus unless it ⁶ _____ (be) absolutely straight. Then attach the lenses inside the tube. You can just slide them in, but if you ⁷ _____ (need) to make them secure, glue them in carefully. Finally, cover the other end of the tube with a piece of cardboard and make a small hole to look through.

Now you're ready to look at the stars! It's not the world's most powerful telescope, but if you ⁸ _____ (use) it on a clear night, you get some good views. If I ⁹ _____ (not have) mine, I wouldn't see nearly so much of the night sky.

5.3 Reading and Vocabulary

Tourists in space

1 Match the sentence halves.

1. [c] Do you think space
2. [ ] Yuri Gagarin was the first space
3. [ ] Several companies have started test
4. [ ] If you go outside, you need to wear this space
5. [ ] The new space
6. [ ] Would you like to be a space

a plane looks amazing.
b traveller in 1961.
c ~~tourism will become popular in the future?~~
d suit to protect you.
e flights for people to go into space.
f tourist?

2 Read the article. Put the topics a–f in the order they are mentioned.

a [ ] examples of effects on your body
b [ ] mental health
c [ ] space walks
d [ ] physical fitness
e [ ] what to do in zero gravity
f [ ] making a mess

3 Read the article again and choose the correct answer.

1. What does the writer say about space tourism in the first paragraph?
   a It will probably become more expensive.
   b More people will consider it in the future.
   c They don't want to try it.
2. How fit should you be to travel in space?
   a extremely fit   b reasonably fit
   c not fit
3. What does the writer recommend you do in zero gravity?
   a spin around   b eat and drink
   c look out into space
4. Which activity does the writer NOT say can make a mess?
   a eating   b drinking water
   c brushing your teeth
5. Why won't you be able to do a space walk?
   a It's too expensive.
   b It's too dangerous.
   c It takes too long.

I can understand an article about space travel.

SO YOU WANT TO VISIT SPACE?

With the increase in space tourism and with it set to become even more popular in the future, you'll most likely want to be a space tourist at some point. Who wouldn't? If you're considering travelling to space, then you'll need to read our 'out-of-this-world' advice first. Here's what you need to know.

It's a good idea to hit the gym first. If you want to experience zero gravity, you need to be physically fit. You don't need to be Olympic athlete level, just at a good level. The whole trip will have effects on your body. For this reason, it's a good idea to be checked by a doctor first. You also need to be mentally fit as this is a life-changing experience that you'll want to enjoy to the full. So keep your brain sharp by learning new skills such as playing a musical instrument.

You need to plan your time there too. Most commercial space tourist flights will only give you a few minutes in zero gravity, so plan what you're going to do because you don't want to waste precious time. And while you might want to spin around or pretend you're flying, include some time just to look out of the window and enjoy the wonderful view too.

When you're in zero gravity, there's no force pulling you down like on Earth, and you might feel dizzy and a bit sick, so be prepared for that. Also, when you leave the Earth's atmosphere (and on re-entry), there will be strong forces pushing and pulling you (most space planes re-enter the atmosphere at nearly 30,000 kilometres per hour). If you suffer from travel sickness, take some medicine with you!

It's important to remember that space travel can be messy. Things we do without thinking on Earth, like drinking water and brushing our teeth, can be difficult to do in space, with no gravity to keep things safe. So make sure you keep containers closed when possible.

Finally, as much as you might want to, you won't be able to put on a space suit and do a space walk. The risks of this are so high that they require weeks of training. After all, if you come loose and float away, there's nobody out there to help you! So remember that while space travel is exciting, you'll need to do a lot of preparation first.

On the Portal
Extra Practice Activities: Lesson 5.3

5.4 Grammar
Third Conditional

GRAMMAR — Third Conditional

Unreal situations in the past
if + Past Perfect, *would* + *have* + past participle
If the lander's solar panels **had been** in sunlight, it **would have been** OK. (They weren't in sunlight.)

1 ● Complete the sentences with the words below. There is one extra word.

| had | hadn't | ~~have~~ | if | left | would | wouldn't |

1 If I hadn't studied Engineering, I wouldn't *have* become interested in space travel.
2 We wouldn't have reached the moon late if we'd _____ Earth on time.
3 _____ the captain hadn't been ill, he wouldn't have left the mission.
4 Would you have been disappointed if you _____ passed the physical exam?
5 I _____ have become an astronaut if I hadn't learned to fly a plane.
6 If they had landed two seconds earlier, they _____ have crashed.

2 ●● Choose the correct option.

What would have happened?
Have you ever had any moments when something bad happened, but something good came out of it? Tell us about it below.

Amy_D: Last year, I had to leave my school because we moved to another city. It was terrible to leave all my friends, but if I'd stayed there, I ¹ *would I* (*wouldn't*) have met my friend Kate. She's been my best friend for three months now and she's great!

BeeZ23: Yesterday, I woke up late and missed the bus for school, so I had to take my bicycle. But I would have been even later if I ² *took / 'd taken* the bus because there was a terrible traffic jam!

SimmSon: For our Science project last month, my teacher made me work with someone I didn't like. If she hadn't made us work together though, we wouldn't ³ *have become / become* friends.

Jenn.if.er: Last week, I was at a party when my dad arrived to pick me up – so embarrassing! But when we got home, I realised that the last bus had left before he arrived, so I would have been stuck if he ⁴ *hadn't come / didn't come*!

3 ●● Match the sentence halves. Then complete the sentences with the correct form of the verbs in brackets.

1 [d] I would have come and found you
2 [ ] If Ollie had saved more money,
3 [ ] They wouldn't have bought the telescope
4 [ ] If I'd been with you,
5 [ ] If we'd known it was going to be so cold,

a I _____ (not let) you buy that expensive jacket.
b we _____ (wear) warmer clothes.
c he _____ (be able) to buy those trainers.
d if I *'d known* (know) you were at the party.
e if it _____ (not be) so cheap.

4 ●●● Choose the correct answer.

An amazing rescue

On 11 April 1970, Apollo 13 flew into space from Florida, USA. If the mission ¹___ successful, Apollo 13 would have been the third manned spacecraft to land on the moon. However, after two days, there was an explosion. If an oxygen tank ²___ exploded, the spacecraft would ³___ landed on the moon. But instead, the mission stopped and the spacecraft orbited the moon. The flight director, Gene Kranz, wanted to use the moon's gravity to push the spacecraft back to Earth. If he hadn't ⁴___ this decision, the astronauts ⁵___ survived. One of the biggest problems of the return journey was removing carbon dioxide from the spacecraft. If engineers on Earth ⁶___ invented a system to do this quickly, the astronauts wouldn't have ⁷___ able to breathe. Finally, on 17 April, the astronauts returned safely to Earth.

1 a was   b were   (c) had been
2 a hadn't   b wouldn't   c hasn't
3 a had   b haven't   c have
4 a make   b made   c making
5 a wouldn't have b would have   c hadn't had
6 a hadn't   b had   c wouldn't
7 a had   b been   c be

I can use the Third Conditional to talk about unreal situations in the past.

On the Portal
Extra Practice Activities: Lesson 5.4

5.5 Listening and Vocabulary
Space debris

1 Read the sentences and write the words in the crossword. What is the hidden word?

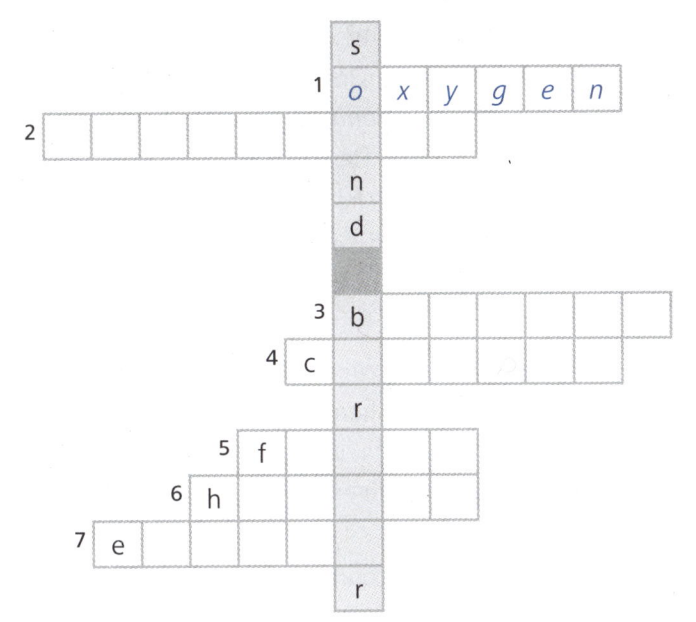

```
        s
      1 o x y g e n
    2 _ _ _ _ _
        n
        d
      3 b _ _ _ _ _
    4 c _ _
        r
      5 f _ _
    6 h _ _ _ _ _
  7 e _ _ _ _
        r
```

1 We need this gas to breathe.
2 This large piece of material fills with air and helps the wearer fall slowly to the ground.
3 A large bag filled with gas or air so that it can float in the air.
4 The part of a spacecraft which contains the astronauts.
5 Physical power which moves something.
6 A gas which is lighter than air and is often used to make things float.
7 A machine which produces power to make a vehicle move.

The hidden word is: _____ .

2 Complete the words in the sentences.
1 After jumping from the plane, Sam opened his pa_r__a__c__h__u__t__e_ and soon landed safely on the ground.
2 The f_ _ _ _e astronauts feel when they take off from Earth is very powerful.
3 The astronauts all felt nervous as the c_ _ s_ _ _ _ left the rest of the spacecraft.
4 We need o_ _ g_ _ _ to breathe.
5 The car has a very powerful _ _n_ _i_ _ _ and can go from 0 to 100 kilometres per hour in nine seconds.
6 If you travel faster than 767 kilometres per hour, you break the s_ _ _ _d b_ _ _ _ _ _r.

I can understand a podcast about space debris.

3 🔊 **5.1** Listen to the first part of a podcast and choose the correct answer.

What is space debris?
a a type of satellite
b parts of old spaceships, satellites, etc. orbiting the Earth
c everything that's in orbit around the Earth

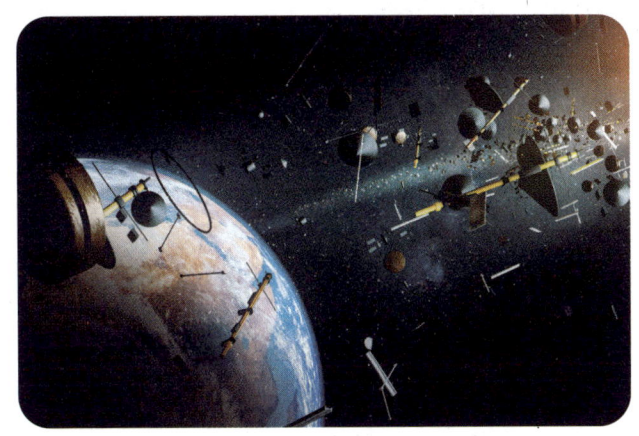

4 🔊 **5.2** Listen to the rest of the podcast and tick the topics which are mentioned.
1 ☐ the number of small pieces of debris
2 ☐ the problems large debris can cause
3 ☐ missions to other planets
4 ☐ the most dangerous area
5 ☐ space debris falling to Earth
6 ☐ Earth's orbit around the Sun
7 ☐ cleaning up the debris

5 🔊 **5.2** Listen again and complete the notes.

Space debris
- more than [1] *170* million pieces of debris smaller than 1 cm
- just one piece of debris can damage a [2] _____ or satellite
- International Space Station (ISS) uses Whipple shields to make debris [3] _____
- nearly 30,000 pieces larger than [4] _____ cm
- some larger pieces can survive the [5] _____ temperatures of the atmosphere
- on average, one piece has landed on Earth every day for last [6] _____ years
- we don't clean it up because it's too [7] _____

On the Portal
Extra Practice Activities: Lesson 5.5

53 Unit 5

5.6 Speaking
Instructions

1 🔊 5.3 Listen and repeat the phrases.

SPEAKING — Instructions

Giving instructions
First, open the app.   Second, point your phone at the sky.
After a few minutes,/After that,/Then/Next, watch what happens.
The last thing you need to do is/Finally, record the result.
Never/Always check the program.
You/We need to check the light is on.
I/We have to check the light is on.
It's important (not) to/Try (not) to fly it fast.

Responding to instructions
That seems fun/easy.   Of course.   OK.
Sure.   No worries.   No problem.
What next?   Now what?   Then what do I do?
I hope it works/I get it right.

2 Match the sentence halves.

1 [b] First,
2 [ ] After
3 [ ] Raise the drone slowly. Try not
4 [ ] Try simple moves at first. After a
5 [ ] That seems
6 [ ] Then what

a to lift it up too fast.
b ~~turn the drone on.~~
c few minutes, you can try something more difficult.
d do I do?
e easy.
f that, open the app on your phone too.

3 Complete the dialogues with the words below.

| always   hope   important   need   ~~second~~ |

1 A: What do I do after that?
   B: _Second_, check all the pieces are there.
2 A: How do I use this laptop?
   B: Just turn it on – there's no password. But you _____ to shut it down when you've finished.
3 A: It's _____ to read the instructions first.
   B: Yes, of course.
4 A: And finally, put this piece on top.
   B: OK, I _____ I get it right!
5 A: Do I make a hole here?
   B: Yes, but _____ use safety glasses to protect your eyes.

4 Choose the correct option.

Gran: Can you help me install an app on my phone, Tom?
Tom: Of course, Gran, let me see. OK, so ¹(first)/ second, you need to open the app store. Here it is.
Gran: OK, that ²checks / seems easy.
Tom: After ³that / next, you need to search for the name of the app in the search bar. See?
Gran: OK. Then what ⁴will / do I do?
Tom: You see where it says 'Get'? Just tap on that. But ⁵never / always check it's a free app, not an expensive one you have to pay for.
Gran: ⁶Of / For course. I don't want to pay for apps!

5 🔊 5.4 Complete the dialogue with one word in each gap. Listen and check.

Chris: Why on earth are you pointing your phone at the sky, Tiana?
Tiana: It's this new app. It lets you identify planets and stars.
Chris: Really? How does it work?
Tiana: ¹_First_, you open the app, like this. ²_____, you point it at a part of the sky. See? There's the moon.
Chris: That ³_____ easy. Can you search for specific things?
Tiana: Sure. What do you want to see?
Chris: Um … Jupiter.
Tiana: ⁴_____ worries. We just type it in here … Oops! Obviously, I ⁵_____ to spell it properly, of course!
Chris: Ha! Yes, that helps. ⁶_____ what do I do?
Tiana: You see that arrow? You need ⁷_____ move the phone in that direction until you see Jupiter.
Chris: Oh yeah, there it is! This app is cool! I'm going to download it.
Tiana: Have fun! But ⁸_____ point it at the sun. If you use it in the daytime, it'll hurt your eyes.

I can give and respond to instructions.

On the Portal
Extra Practice Activities: Lesson 5.6

5.7 Writing
A for and against essay

1 Read the essay quickly and choose the best title.
  a Should we send people to Mars?
  b Is space exploration a good thing?
  c Which planet should we visit next?

---

① ¹*Many people believe* that the next step in space exploration is sending astronauts to Mars. It sounds exiting, but ² _____ it?

② ³ _____ , we might discover things we need on Earth, like oil or gas. ⁴ _____ , we already know that there is a lot of methane gas on Mars, and it can be used to make plastic. ⁵ _____ we could discover new forms of life. ⁶ _____ there is frozen water on Mars and possibly even running water. This may mean there are other forms of life there.

③ ⁷ _____ , a manned mission to Mars would be incredibly expensive, at over $50 billion. The spacecraft would need to take food, water, oxygen and medical supplies, and these things would have to be launched into space. ⁸ _____ we could spend this money on solving the problems we already have on Earth. ⁹ _____ , it's very dangerous. We don't know the effects of being in space and of weightlessness on the human body for such a long period of time. In ¹⁰ _____ , the possible human cost is too great a risk.

④ ¹¹ _____ , while living on Mars might seem like a good idea, I think we have big problems to solve on Earth first.

---

2 Complete gaps 1–6 in the essay with phrases a–f.
  a For example
  b ~~Many people believe~~
  c It seems
  d Another advantage is that
  e is it worth
  f On the one hand

3 Complete gaps 7–11 in the essay with phrases a–e.
  a my opinion   d On the other hand
  b To sum up   e Moreover
  c I believe

4 Look at the essay in Exercise 1 again and number the parts of it 1–4.
  advantages ☐   conclusion ☐
  disadvantages ☐ introduction ☐

5 Match the sentence halves.
  1 [c] To sum   4 ☐ The main
  2 ☐ One reason for   5 ☐ Finally, it could
  3 ☐ Nowadays more and

  a disadvantage is a lack of technology.
  b be a stepping stone for further space exploration.
  c ~~up, I believe space exploration is a good idea.~~
  d doing this is to find another planet to live on.
  e more people believe we should travel in space.

6 Complete the notes with the words and phrases below.

  dangerous   expensive   new forms   population
  problems   ~~to save~~

  Should we spend money on finding another planet to live on?
  For:
  • might not be able ¹*to save* this planet
  • discover ² _____ of life
  • growing ³ _____ on Earth and limited space
  Against:
  • too ⁴ _____ – billions of dollars
  • ⁵ _____ on Earth more urgent
  • too ⁶ _____ – could die in space

WRITING TIME

7 Write an essay answering the question in Exercise 6.

1 Find ideas
  Make notes for your essay. Think about:
  • a short introduction and conclusion.
  • your reasons for and against, and your final decision.

2 Plan and write
  • Organise your ideas into paragraphs. Use the essay in Exercise 1 to help you.
  • Write a draft of your essay.

3 Check
  • Check language: have you used linkers of addition?
  • Check grammar: have you used any conditionals?
  • Write the final version of your essay.

I can write an essay discussing advantages and disadvantages. **55** Unit 5

My Language File

WORDLIST 🔊 5.5

Space
- astronaut (n) _____
- astronomer (n) _____
- comet (n) _____
- Earth (n) _____
- galaxy (n) _____
- gravity (n) _____
- moon (n) _____
- orbit (n) _____
- planet (n) _____
- satellite (n) _____
- solar system (n) _____
- space station (n) _____
- star (n) _____
- telescope (n) _____

Word friends
(dimensions and distance)
- 10 km per hour _____
- be 10 cm high/long/wide _____
- be 10 km away/from _____
- height (n) _____
- length (n) _____
- speed (n) _____
- width (n) _____

Large numbers
- 100 = hundred (n) _____
- 1,000 = thousand (n) _____
- 1,000,000 = million (n) _____
- 1,000,000,000 = billion (n) _____

Space travel
- flight simulator (n) _____
- space plane (n) _____
- space suit (n) _____
- space tourism (n) _____
- space tourist (n) _____
- space traveller (n) _____
- test flight (n) _____
- zero gravity (n) _____

Space science
- balloon (n) _____
- capsule (n) _____
- engine (n) _____
- force (n) _____
- helium (n) _____
- oxygen (n) _____
- parachute (n) _____
- sound barrier (n) _____

Extra words
- analysis (n) _____
- appear (v) _____
- atmosphere (n) _____
- bright stars (n) _____
- calculation (n) _____
- data (n) _____
- discovery (n) _____
- dust (n) _____
- experiment (n) _____
- float (v) _____
- footprint (n) _____
- free fall (n) _____
- globe (n) _____
- ground (n) _____
- jet plane (n) _____
- land (v) _____
- landing module (n) _____
- manned flight (n) _____
- Mars (n) _____
- Mercury (n) _____
- mission (n) _____
- mystery (n) _____
- on board _____
- orbit (v) _____
- push limits _____
- record breaker (n) _____
- robot (n) _____
- rover (n) _____
- scientific achievement (n) _____
- scientist (n) _____
- signal (n) _____
- skydiver (n) _____
- solar panel (n) _____
- sound wave (n) _____
- space rubbish (n) _____
- space science (n) _____
- spacecraft (n) _____
- spaceship (n) _____
- speed of sound (n) _____
- surface (n) _____
- universe (n) _____
- Venus (n) _____
- visible (adj) _____

Sounds good!
- Let's go for it! _____
- It looks good. _____
- Phew! _____

MY LANGUAGE NOTES

My favourite words/expressions from this unit

Self-check

Vocabulary

1 Complete the sentences with the words below. There is one extra word.

> comet   engine   galaxy   gravity   orbit
> satellite   star

1. The jet _____ makes it fly very fast.
2. The recent mission sent a _____ into space to improve communication systems in Europe.
3. There are billions of stars in our _____.
4. The Earth takes one year to _____ the Sun.
5. The Sun is a giant _____.
6. _____ is what makes things fall to the ground.

2 Write the correct word for each definition.

1. the word for 1,000,000: a m_ _ _ _ _ _
2. someone who studies the stars: a_ _ _ _ _ _ _ _ _ _
3. an icy rock travelling through space with a 'tail' of gas: c_ _ _ _
4. ours has eight planets in it: s_ _ _ _ _ s_ _ _ _ _
5. the measurement of how wide something is: w_ _ _ _
6. something you use to look at the stars: t_ _ _ _ _ _ _ _ _
7. the measurement of how high something is: h_ _ _ _ _
8. the Earth is one of these: p_ _ _ _ _

3 Choose the correct option.

1. The Sun is around 150 million kilometres *from / away* Earth.
2. The satellite is 30 metres *length / long*.
3. They travel at 10,000 kilometres *the / an* hour.
4. It costs seven thousand, five hundred *or / and* twenty pounds.
5. The space mission cost two point *eight / eight hundred* million euros.
6. How *height / high* can modern planes fly?

Grammar

4 Choose the correct option.

1. If we *have / had* the money, we'd buy a car.
2. If I'm not too tired after school, I usually *go / would go* cycling in the park.
3. I wouldn't *meet / have met* Anna if I hadn't gone to the party.
4. Louis *won't come / will come* to the picnic unless the weather is good.
5. I wouldn't call Ann if I *am / were* you.
6. If my team *would win / wins* the championship, I'll dance in the street!
7. If we *had left / left* earlier, we wouldn't have missed the bus.
8. You break the sound barrier if you *travel / had travelled* faster than 340 metres per second.

5 Complete the text with the correct form of the verbs in brackets.

> I want to be an astronaut. I know it's very ambitious, but I'm sure if I work really hard, I [1]_____ (achieve) my dream one day. If I have any free time, I [2]_____ (study) Physics. When people ask me, 'What would you do if you [3]_____ (win) the lottery?', the answer is easy: I [4]_____ (travel) to space! I know I [5]_____ (not be) allowed to go unless I'm physically fit too, so I [6]_____ (play) sport. What about you? If you could do any job at all, what [7]_____ (you/do)?

Speaking

6 Choose the correct answer.

1. The last ____ you need to do is take the photo.
   a thing   b problem   c check
2. After a ____ minutes, check your emails.
   a some   b few   c time
3. It's important ____ the lights when you leave.
   a turn off   b turning off   c to turn off
4. Try ____ park in that road after 9 a.m.
   a not to   b don't to   c don't
5. That ____ easy.
   a sure   b not   c seems

YOUR SCORE

Vocabulary: __/20   Speaking: __/5
Grammar: __/15   Total: __/40

Good health

VOCABULARY
Health problems | First aid kit |
Word building: health and illness |
Health improvement | Extreme sports

GRAMMAR
Reported statements and
questions | Reported commands
and requests

6   6.1   Vocabulary
Sickness and health

1 ● Match the words below with the descriptions.

| asthma   broken bone   cut   ~~ear infection~~   fever |
| migraine   rash   virus |

1 My ear really hurts. *ear infection*
2 My hand slipped when I was using a knife and there's blood. _____
3 I've got a really high temperature. _____
4 Sometimes it's very difficult for me to breathe. _____
5 My skin is red and sore. _____
6 My head hurts, I have a pain behind my eyes and I feel sick. _____
7 Someone sneezed near me and now I don't feel well. _____
8 I fell off my bike and now my arm is in plaster. _____

2 ●● Read what the people say and complete the words for health problems.

1 Oh no, your leg is a strange shape! That looks like a b _r_ _o_ _k_ _e_ _n_   b _o_ _n_ _e_!
2 What happened?! You've got a big b_ _ _ _ on your head.
3 I feel terrible – I think I've got a v_ _ _ _.
4 I love going for country walks, but I sometimes get covered in i_ _ _ _ b_ _ _ _ from the mosquitoes!
5 I'm recovering from a c_ _ _ i_ _ _ _ _ _ _ and I still find it hard to breathe.
6 Your temperature is forty degrees. You've got a f_ _ _ _.

3 ● **WORD FRIENDS** Match verbs 1–6 with words/phrases a–f.

1 *b* make   a your voice
2 ☐ lose   b ~~an appointment~~
3 ☐ take   c a bone
4 ☐ feel   d an operation
5 ☐ have   e dizzy
6 ☐ break   f your temperature

4 ●● Complete the sentences with a word from box A and a word/phrase from box B.

A | describe   emergency   ~~fall~~   get   getting   hurt   lost |

B | appetite   blood test   ~~ill~~   leg   prescription   symptoms   treatment |

1 If you *fall ill*, don't come to school.
2 I don't want anything to eat, thanks. I've _____ my _____.
3 I'm Dr Fox. How are you feeling? Can you _____ your _____ to me?
4 I need to see the doctor so I can _____ a _____ for my blood pressure medicine.
5 I _____ my _____ when I fell over and now I can't walk very well.
6 Call an ambulance! He needs to get _____ _____!
7 I'm going to the doctor's today. Don't worry, nothing's wrong. I'm just _____ a _____.

Unit 6   58

5 ● Choose the correct option.
1. I always clean the kitchen surfaces with an (antibacterial) / antiseptic spray.
2. Take two of these *pills / bandages* twice a day, with food.
3. Can you get me some cough *cream / medicine*?
4. Put the *cream / thermometer* under your arm for three minutes so I can take your temperature.
5. Here, put this sticking *plaster / bandage* on that cut.
6. My foot really hurts. I need some *painkillers / cough medicine*, I think.

6 ●● Write the correct word for each definition.
1. You take some of this if you have a cough.
   c<u>o u g h</u> m<u>e d i c i n e</u>
2. You put this round your wrist if it's painful to move it. b___ ___ ___ ___ ___ ___ ___
3. You use this to take your temperature.
   t___ ___ ___ ___ ___ ___ ___ ___ ___ ___
4. You can take these if you have a bad headache. p___ ___ ___ ___ ___ ___ ___ ___ ___ ___
5. You put this on a small cut.
   s___ ___ ___ ___ ___ ___ ___   p___ ___ ___ ___ ___ ___ ___
6. You put this on insect bites.
   a___ ___ ___ ___ ___ ___ ___ ___ ___ ___ ___   c___ ___ ___ ___ ___

7 ● Complete the table.

Noun	Verb	Adjective
allergy	–	¹*allergic*
2	3	infected
4	–	ill
pain	–	5
6	operate	–

I can talk about health problems.

8 ●● Complete the sentences with the correct form of the words below.

| allergy | blind | ~~infect~~ | injure | operate | pain |

1. 'The place where I cut myself is red and sore.'
   'I think you've got an *infection*.'
2. I went into hospital to have a(n) _____ on my leg.
3. Avoid contact with eyes. This product can cause _____.
4. I can't move my leg – it's too _____.
5. I can't eat nuts because I'm _____ to them.
6. Rob got a nasty leg _____ in the accident.

9 ●●● Complete the blog post with one word in each gap.

Nuts about nuts

On Saturday, I woke up feeling really awful. I had ¹*lost* my appetite and I felt sick. My mum ² _____ my temperature. I had a fever, and she also saw I ³ _____ a rash all over my face and neck. She thought it might be an ⁴ _____, so she immediately called the doctor's to ⁵ _____ for an appointment, and we got one immediately. When we got there, the doctor asked me to ⁶ _____ my symptoms. I showed her the rash. I also told her it's ⁷ _____ when I swallow. In the end, she told me I have a food ⁸ _____ – I'm ⁹ _____ to nuts. She gave me a ¹⁰ _____ to take to the chemist's and told me to stay in bed until I felt better.

On the Portal
Extra Practice Activities: Lesson 6.1

6.2 Grammar
Reported statements and questions

GRAMMAR — Reported statements and questions

Present Simple → Past Simple
'I have a headache.' → He said (that) he had a headache.

Present Continuous → Past Continuous
'I'm getting better.' → She said (that) she was getting better.

Past Simple → Past Perfect
'I left home at six.' → He said (that) he had left home at six.

will → would
'My mum will do it.' → He said (that) his mum would do it.

can → could
'I can't see anything.' → She said (that) she couldn't see anything.

Questions
'What time is it?' → He asked what time it was.
'Do you know Dr Lee?' → She asked me if/whether I knew Dr Lee.

Changing pronouns, time phrases and place adverbials
now → then   here → there
this month → that month
yesterday → the previous day/the day before
tomorrow → the next/following day
'My dad was here yesterday.' → He said (that) his dad had been there the day before.

1 ● Match direct statements and questions 1–5 with reported speech a–e.
1 [c] 'I'm having a check-up.'
2 [ ] 'Are you having a check-up?'
3 [ ] 'I'll have a check-up.'
4 [ ] 'I had a check-up.'
5 [ ] 'What time is your check-up?'

a She told me she would have a check-up.
b She asked me what time my check-up was.
c ~~She said she was having a check-up.~~
d She asked me if I was having a check-up.
e She said she'd had a check-up.

2 ● Choose the correct option.
1 My dad asked me what time *was my appointment* / (*my appointment was.*)
2 She said she had seen the doctor *the day before / yesterday*.
3 Charles asked me if *I had got / had I got* the results of my blood test yet.
4 After the injury, Linda said she *can't / couldn't* feel her arm.

3 ●● Rewrite the statements and questions in reported speech.

Who do you think will win the World Cup?
1 She asked us *who we thought would win the World Cup*.

I want to be a scientist.
2 He said _____.

I went to the doctor yesterday.
3 She said _____.

What can we do to help Liam pass his exams?
4 He asked us _____.

I'm having a party this weekend.
5 She told us _____.

Do you study Biology at school?
6 He asked me _____.

4 ●●● Choose the correct answer.

The other day, my sister Charis and her husband told me some excellent news. They said they ¹____ a baby, and that I ²____ an uncle! They said they ³____ out the week before, but wanted to be sure everything was OK before they told me. The doctor said he ⁴____ worried at first because my sister ⁵____ ill recently, but he checked carefully and the baby is healthy. They asked me ⁶____ any ideas about her name. I told them I ⁷____ to call her Carla because my name's Carl. Unfortunately, they said they ⁸____ that idea!

1 a had   b had had   (c) were having
2 a are soon   b was soon   c would soon be
3 a would find   b had found   c were finding
4 a had been   b will be   c would be
5 a is   b will be   c had been
6 a if I had   b did I have   c if I was having
7 a will want   b would want   c had wanted
8 a didn't like   b weren't liking c hadn't liked

Unit 6 — I can report what somebody else has said.

On the Portal — Extra Practice Activities: Lesson 6.2

6.3 Reading and Vocabulary

Mental well-being

1 Complete the advert with the correct form of the words below.

| avoid | count | give | ~~have~~ | make | manage |
| measure | show | stay | take | | |

Improve your health with Routic

Feeling low? Need to get in shape? Looking for ways to ¹*have* more energy throughout the day? ² _____ calm and download the **Routic app**. Routic lets you ³ _____ control of your health and fitness. It ⁴ _____ your walking route when you're out and about, and ⁵ _____ your steps. It also ⁶ _____ your speed and heart rate. If you have a health condition, it can help you ⁷ _____ your symptoms, and it ⁸ _____ you cooking advice if you need to ⁹ _____ certain foods. This one app does it all and can really ¹⁰ _____ a big difference. **Download it today!**

2 Read the article quickly and tick (✓) the things it mentions.

1. ☐ family
2. ☐ animals
3. ☐ apps
4. ☐ school work
5. ☐ gardening
6. ☐ cooking
7. ☐ sport

3 Read the article again and complete the sentences. Use no more than three words.

1. According to the article, our *mental health* is as important as our physical health.
2. Nancy says that your _____ drops when you stroke a cat or dog.
3. Gardening can help you become more _____.
4. The _____ in fresh food are good for your physical and mental well-being.
5. Taking on too many new things can cause _____.
6. Some apps can help you stay calm by teaching you how to use _____.

Healthy mind, healthy body

We all know that it's important to be fit and healthy. People tell us to eat well and do exercise, but our mental health is just as important. There are many easy, practical ways to improve our mental well-being. We spoke to psychologist Nancy Nguyen about how we can do this.

Make a four-legged friend

The first thing Nancy suggests is becoming friends with an animal. She had a dog when she was a teenager, and told us about a time when she had a problem with another girl at school. She said she had come home one day and just sat with her dog, and it made her feel much better. She said she had felt better almost immediately. We've known for a long time that having a pet is good for you. Just stroking a dog or cat can lower your heart rate and help you stay calm. If you don't have a pet, you could offer to walk a neighbour's dog or volunteer at the nearest animal shelter.

Turn your fingers green

It's not just animals which can make you feel better: plants can too. Doing some gardening is another method you can use to improve your mental well-being. Nancy explained how you can start with something simple like a tomato plant. You can learn how to grow it by researching it online, and watch it grow from a seed to a fruit. She described how peaceful the process is and how it teaches us to be patient.

Get creative in the kitchen

Once you've grown your own food, put it to good use in the kitchen. If you don't already, then learn how to cook. Choose the food you like and learn some simple recipes. This will improve what you eat and make you feel good when you manage to cook a new dish for the first time. Once you learn a few basics, you can then get creative and try out new things. Being creative is a great way to keep your mind fit and healthy, and the nutrients from fresh food also improve your overall well-being.

Don't overdo it

There are many things you can do to improve your wellness, but whatever you decide to do, don't take on too much. While it's important to have interests outside school, don't overload yourself. This alone can create unnecessary stress.

Add a tech touch

Nancy also recommends using a special app. There are many free apps available which can help you develop routines and take control of your mental health. For example, they can help you manage negative thoughts or use breathing techniques to stay calm. There's even one which lets you create music to reflect how you feel. Using an app like this allows you to put all of these techniques together in one handy place.

I can understand an article about mental well-being.

6.4 Grammar
Reported commands and requests

GRAMMAR — Reported commands and requests

Commands
'Do more exercise.' → She told him to do more exercise.
'Don't worry!' → She told me not to worry.

Requests
'Can you give me something, please?' → I asked the doctor to give me something.
'Please don't shout!' → She asked him not to shout.

1 ● Complete the reported commands and requests with the words below.

| asked | me | not | to | ~~told~~ | us |

1 'Put it down.'
   She _told_ me to put it down.
2 'Lie down, please.'
   The doctor _____ me to lie down.
3 'Everybody, listen carefully, please.'
   The teacher asked _____ to listen carefully.
4 'Don't work too hard.'
   He told us _____ to work too hard.
5 'Lift your arm, please.'
   The nurse asked _____ to lift my arm.
6 'Fill in the form.'
   The receptionist told me _____ fill in the form.

2 ● Choose the correct option.
1 Dad: Hey! I asked you (not to be) / to not be so loud up here, please.
  Molly: Sorry, Dad. It's just that Jane *asked me* / *asked* to help her with her Music project.
  Dad: OK, but turn the volume down, will you? Mum's got a headache and she asked us *not to* / *to not* make any noise.
2 Meg: Jamie, can you help me with my Maths homework? I *told* / *asked* Dad to help, but he's busy.
  Jamie: Sure. What do you have to do?
  Meg: Well, the teacher told us *to do* / *do* the exercises on this page, but I just don't understand them.

3 ●● Use the prompts to write reported commands and requests.
1 the teacher / ask / we / listen / carefully
   The teacher asked us to listen carefully.
2 Freya / tell / we / not leave / rubbish / in her car
   _____
3 I / ask / they / sit / over there
   _____
4 the doctor / tell / me / not play / sport / for two weeks
   _____
5 Sarah / ask / Kate / meet / she / after school
   _____

4 ●●● Complete the text with reported commands and requests. Use the prompts in brackets.

What I did in an emergency

Last week, I was with my friend Joel when he said he was in pain and he ¹*asked me to call* (ask / I / call) an ambulance. I called 999 and the woman on the phone ² _____ (ask / I / describe) the problem. She also ³ _____ (ask / I / tell) her if Joel was taking any medicine. I said he wasn't. Then she ⁴ _____ (tell / I / make) sure he was comfortable, so I ⁵ _____ (tell / he / sit down) and not move. The woman on the phone said the ambulance would be there in a few minutes and ⁶ _____ (tell / I / not panic), which was difficult! When the ambulance arrived, they took Joel to hospital and I ⁷ _____ (ask / they / let) me come too. When we got there, they told me he had an ear infection and ⁸ _____ (ask / I / phone) his parents. In the end, they gave him some pills and a prescription, and he was fine a couple of days later.

6.5 Listening and Vocabulary

Extreme sports

1 Look at the pictures and complete the words for extreme sports.

1 B*MXing*
2 p_____ 
3 h_____-g_____ 
4 s_____ 
5 k_____ 
6 a_____ 
7 f_____r_____ 
8 p_____ 
9 w_____r_____ 
10 z_____ 

2 Complete what the people say with the names of extreme sports.

1 I tried s*andboarding* for the first time on holiday. We went really fast down the dunes in the desert. It was really exciting!

2 P_____ is really scary at first, but as soon as you jump out of the plane, you forget to be afraid and you just enjoy the view.

3 I've been into B_____ since I got my first bike at the age of five. It's great fun to compete in races and it's a good way to see the countryside.

4 I could never do a_____. I hate high places, so the idea of going down a rock with a rope seems terrifying to me.

5 K_____ is great fun, but if it's not windy enough, then you get very wet when you fall into the sea!

6 I've done z_____ once – I went really fast from the top of a hill and landed on the beach. It was amazing!

3 🔊 6.1 Listen to Kieran talking about a summer sports camp. Put the sports in the order he talks about them. There is one extra sport.

a ☐ abseiling   d ☐ BMXing
b ☐ kitesurfing   e ☐ sandboarding
c ☐ whitewater rafting

4 🔊 6.1 Listen again and complete the notes.

SSC
- SSC = Summer Sports ¹*Camp*
- how long: ² _____ weeks
- BMXing: learn how to go ³ _____, even up hills
- abseiling: first, practise on the ⁴ _____ wall
- whitewater rafting: train for a day before practising on the ⁵ _____
- check our health with a short ⁶ _____
- book by: ⁷ _____ June
- cost: ⁸ £ _____ – includes food, ⁹ _____ and equipment

I can understand a talk about extreme sports.

6.6 Speaking
Asking for and giving advice

1 🔊 **6.2** Listen and repeat the phrases.

> **SPEAKING** — Asking for and giving advice
>
> **Asking for advice**
> What do you think I should do?
> If you were me, what would you do?
> What shall I do?   Should I keep my head up?
> Have you got any ideas (what to do)?
>
> **Giving advice**
> If I were you, I'd make a doctor's appointment.
> You'd better/It might be a good idea to lean forward.
> You should/ought to/need to put your foot up.
> Let's rest.
> Have you tried/thought about putting some ice on it?
> Try pressing your nose.
> I'd recommend/advise/suggest taking an aspirin.
>
> **Being unable to give advice**
> I don't know what to advise/suggest/do, I'm afraid.
> I wish I could help, but I'm not sure what's best.
> I'm afraid I can't really help you.

2 Match questions 1–5 with responses a–e.
1. [d] I've got a fever. What's your advice?
2. [ ] I've hurt my arm. Any ideas what to do?
3. [ ] I've cut my finger. If you were me, what would you do?
4. [ ] I've got a weird rash on my arm. What do you suggest?
5. [ ] I've got a migraine. Any ideas what to do?

a If I were you, I'd stop playing on your computer.
b Try putting some cream on it.
c I'd recommend taking some painkillers.
d ~~Have you tried staying in bed and rest?~~
e You should put a sticking plaster on it.

3 Complete the sentences with the correct form of the verbs in brackets.
1. Have you tried *taking* (take) vitamin C?
2. What shall I _____ (do)?
3. Have you got any ideas what _____ (do)?
4. You ought _____ (call) your doctor as soon as possible.
5. If your foot is still painful, try _____ (take) some painkillers.
6. I'd recommend _____ (rest) your arm as much as possible.

4 Choose the correct option.
1. You (ought) / should / better to have a check-up.
2. If you were me, what *do / would / will* you do?
3. I wish I *will / would / could* suggest something, but I can't.
4. Have you thought *on / about / if* eating more healthily?
5. What do you *think / know / shall* I should do?
6. I don't know what to suggest, I'm *frightened / scared / afraid*.
7. It *might / should / shall* be a good idea to see a doctor.
8. You'd *ought / should / better* go to bed until you feel better.

5 🔊 **6.3** Complete the dialogue with one word in each gap. Listen and check.

Liv: What's the matter, Zoe? You look ill.
Zoe: I keep getting these headaches. They get worse when I'm stressed, but I have to study for my exams at the moment. Have you got any ¹*ideas* what to do?
Liv: I'm ² _____ I can't really help you. Have you ³ _____ about asking Ian? I think he had the same problem a few weeks ago.
Zoe: That's a good idea. I'll be seeing him later. Oh, wait, there he is now. Ian, over here!
Ian: Hi, girls! How are things?
Liv: Well, I'm fine, but Zoe here keeps getting headaches. I'm not sure what she should do.
Zoe: That's right. Liv recommended I speak to you. What do you ⁴ _____ I should do?
Ian: You ⁵ _____ take a painkiller.
Zoe: I'd prefer not to, if possible. I don't really like taking medicine.
Ian: Well, maybe you don't drink enough water. It might be a good ⁶ _____ to carry a bottle around with you.
Zoe: Like this, you mean? I drink loads of water!
Ian: Hmm … Well, I don't know what else to suggest, I'm afraid. If I ⁷ _____ you, I ⁸ _____ make an appointment to see the doctor.
Zoe: Yes, I think I will.

I can ask for and give advice.

On the Portal
Extra Practice Activities: Lesson 6.6

6.7 Writing

A forum post about an experience

A learning experience: making pasta
by Liam Sullivan

I've just been on a great course. It was on how to make pasta and it took place at an Italian restaurant. There were ten of us from my class. Our Food Technology teacher encouraged me to take the course.

First of all, our chef, Paolo, told us that hygiene is very important in the kitchen. He explained that we should always wash our hands. He also reminded us to wear an apron.

After that, we went on to make the pasta. Paolo showed us how to mix the ingredients – flour, oil and eggs – with a fork. Next, we made dough with our hands. He warned us not to add water. Finally, he advised us to leave the dough to rest for thirty minutes.

About half an hour later, we were ready to make our pasta. Everybody made a different type. I made fettuccine. Soon after, we were cooking our pasta. It was delicious!

I had never made pasta before. It was a fun learning experience. I highly recommend it to anyone who thinks cooking is difficult.

1 Read Liam's post and answer the questions.
1. What was the course on?
   how to make pasta
2. Who recommended the course?
3. Had Liam made pasta before?
4. Did he enjoy the course?
5. Who does he think this course is good for?

2 Order the reporting verbs as they appear in the Liam's post. There is one extra verb.
- a ☐ asked
- b ☐ explained
- c [1] encouraged
- d ☐ reminded
- e ☐ advised
- f ☐ warned

3 Rewrite the sentences using the reporting verbs in brackets.
1. 'Don't forget to check your writing when you've finished,' the teacher told us. (remind)
   The teacher reminded us to check our writing.
2. 'Don't touch that hot plate,' the waiter told me. (warn)
3. 'This is how you mix the things together,' the chef told us. (explain)
4. 'Make notes as you watch the video,' the trainer told them. (advise)
5. 'You should show your work to your friends,' the tutor told Anna. (encourage)

4 Match paragraph functions 1–5 with example sentences a–e.
1. [d] getting your reader's attention and basic details
2. ☐ describing what happened first
3. ☐ describing what happened next
4. ☐ describing what happened in the end
5. ☐ summary recommendation

a. At the beginning, the trainer explained how to survive in the wild.
b. If you really want to try something different, I encourage you to try it.
c. Eventually, we arrived at our destination.
d. ~~Let me tell you about my outdoor survival course.~~
e. After that, we tried to make a campfire.

WRITING TIME

5 Write a forum post about a real or imaginary learning experience.

1 Find ideas
Make notes about:
- how to get your reader's attention.
- the details of the training/event: what you learned and how you learned it.
- a summary recommendation.

2 Plan and write
- Organise your ideas into paragraphs. Use Liam's post in Exercise 1 to help you.
- Write a draft of your post.

3 Check
- Check language: have you used reporting verbs?
- Check grammar: have you used reported speech correctly?
- Write the final version of your post.

I can write a post about a learning experience.

My Language File

WORDLIST 🔊 6.4

Health problems
asthma (n) _____
broken bone (n) _____
bruise (n) _____
chest/ear/eye infection (n) _____
cut (n) _____
fever (n) _____
insect bite (n) _____
migraine (n) _____
rash (n) _____
virus (n) _____

First aid kit
antibacterial spray (n) _____
antiseptic cream (n) _____
bandage (n) _____
cough medicine (n) _____
painkiller (n) _____
pill (n) _____
sticking plaster (n) _____
thermometer (n) _____

Word friends
(illnesses and accidents)
break a bone _____
fall ill _____
feel dizzy _____
have a serious injury _____
have an accident _____
hurt your arm/back/leg _____
lose your appetite/voice _____
your muscles ache _____

(at the doctor's)
ask for an appointment _____
describe your symptoms _____
get a blood test _____
get a prescription _____
make an appointment _____
take your temperature _____

(at the hospital)
get emergency treatment _____
have an operation _____

Word building
(health and illness)
allergic (adj) _____
allergy (n) _____
blind (adj) _____
blindness (n) _____
deaf (adj) _____
deafness (n) _____
depressed (adj) _____
depression (n) _____
ill (adj) _____
illness (n) _____
infect (v) _____
infection (n) _____
injure (v) _____
injury (n) _____
operate (v) _____
operation (n) _____
pain (n) _____
painful (adj) _____
sick (adj) _____
sickness (n) _____

Health improvement
avoid certain foods _____
count your steps _____
give advice _____
have more energy _____
make a big difference _____
manage your symptoms _____
measure your heart rate _____
measure your speed _____
show a walking route _____
stay calm _____
take control of your health
    and fitness _____

Extreme sports
abseiling (n) _____
BMXing (n) _____
free running (n) _____
hang-gliding (n) _____
kitesurfing (n) _____
paddleboarding (n) _____
parachuting (n) _____
sandboarding (n) _____
whitewater rafting (n) _____
ziplining (n) _____

Extra words
ankle (n) _____
bleed (v) _____
brain (n) _____
chemist's (n) _____
colour blind (adj) _____
condition (n) _____
cough (v) _____
doctor's surgery (n) _____
emergency services (n) _____
eye test (n) _____
faint (v) _____
fall (n) _____
health care (n) _____
lung (n) _____
nosebleed (n) _____
sneeze (v) _____
sore throat (n) _____
stomach ache (n) _____
suffer (an injury) (v) _____
take care of yourself _____

Sounds good!
You carry on. _____
Are you all right? _____
Oh gosh! _____

MY LANGUAGE NOTES

My favourite words/expressions from this unit

Self-check

Vocabulary

1 Complete the sentences with the words below.

> bite   blood test   bones   injury   medicine
> muscles   plasters   spray   symptoms   virus

1. When will I get the results of my _____?
2. Scott has a serious back _____.
3. My _____ are aching after all that tennis!
4. You'll be fine. No broken _____ – just bruises.
5. The doctor said I have that _____ that's going around at the moment.
6. That looks like a nasty insect _____. You need to put some cream on it.
7. What's wrong? Describe your _____ to me.
8. Have we got any sticking _____? I've cut my finger.
9. Try taking this cough _____. It will make you feel better.
10. Use this antibacterial _____ when you clean the cut.

2 Choose the correct option.

1. Imogen's really good at free *boarding / running* – look at her go up that wall!
2. I tried *parachuting / hang-gliding* once, but I was too scared to jump out of the plane!
3. Last weekend, we went whitewater *rafting / boarding*, and I got really wet!
4. When I was in the north of Brazil, I tried *sandboarding / ziplining*. It felt strange doing it on land.
5. You can go *abseiling / paddleboarding* on the lake near where I live.

3 Complete the text with the correct form of the words in brackets.

Last year, I had to go into hospital to have an ¹_____ (operate). I had to take painkillers for a few weeks because it was very ²_____ (pain), but then I got better. However, a couple of weeks later, I became ill again and had to have emergency ³_____ (treat). Nobody knew what my ⁴_____ (ill) was. It was difficult to breathe and I couldn't do much exercise. Finally, they discovered that I was ⁵_____ (allergy) to milk! I now have to avoid it all the time.

Grammar

4 Complete the text reporting the conversation between Harry and the receptionist. Use one word in each gap.

H: Excuse me, my appointment was an hour ago and I'm still waiting.
R: I'm sorry, sir. The doctor is very busy today. I'll call you when she's free.
H: I don't feel well. When will the doctor be ready to see me?
R: I'm sorry, sir, I don't know.

Harry told the receptionist that his appointment ¹_____ been an hour before and he ²_____ still waiting. The receptionist apologised and said the doctor ³_____ very busy ⁴_____ day. He said he ⁵_____ call him when she ⁶_____ free. Harry said he ⁷_____ not feel well and asked when the doctor ⁸_____ be ready to see ⁹_____. The receptionist said he ¹⁰_____ not know.

5 Rewrite the commands and requests in reported speech. Use *told* or *asked* and the words in brackets.

1. 'Stay in bed and get some rest.' (doctor / me)
   _____
2. 'Please help me change my bandage.' (I / my friend)
   _____
3. 'Take the medicine twice a day.' (nurse / him)
   _____
4. 'Be quiet, please.' (Sally / us)
   _____
5. 'Don't touch that.' (Kevin's mum / him)
   _____

Speaking

6 Complete the dialogues with one word in each gap.

1. A: I feel dizzy! Have you got _____ ideas what to do?
   B: If I were _____, I'd go to bed.
2. A: I've got this pain in my leg. What do you think I _____ do?
   B: I wish I could _____, but I can't. It might be a _____ idea to see a doctor.

YOUR SCORE

Vocabulary: __/20   Speaking: __/5
Grammar: __/15   Total: __/40

Reading Time 2

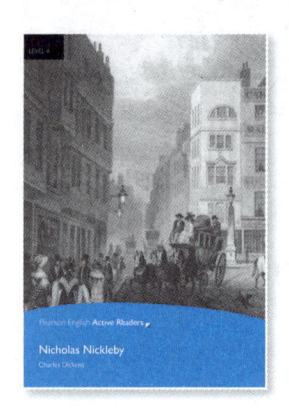

Nicholas Nickleby

After his father's death, Nicholas has no money, no job and a family to support. His only hope is Uncle Ralph, a cold-hearted money-lender with unpleasant, dangerous friends. Can Nicholas and his family find happiness, or will his uncle manage to destroy them?

'You wanted to say something, young man?' he said.

'I was wondering why you were looking at these advertisements,' Nicholas replied.

'Did you think I was looking for work?' Nicholas shook his head. 'Ha! Ha!' laughed the old gentleman. 'A very natural thought, I suppose. I thought the same about you.'

'But I am looking for work,' Nicholas replied.

'What?' the old man said with surprise. 'A well-behaved, polite young gentleman like you? I don't believe it.'

Nicholas told him about the death of his father and the unhappy situation of his poor mother and sister. Before he realised it, he had told the kind old man almost everything about his life. He did not, however, say much about his uncle.

The old man listened with great attention. When Nicholas had finished his story, he said, 'Come along with me. We mustn't lose a minute.'

The old gentleman took Nicholas across London to a quiet square in East London, near the Bank of England, and led him into the oldest, cleanest-looking house in the square. The name Cheeryble Brothers was above the door.

Nicholas followed the old gentleman across a large, busy hall that was filled with boxes of cotton and other material. They went across a yard and into another building. Inside this building, which was the counting-house, an old, large-faced man with silver glasses was sitting at a desk.

'Is my brother in his room, Tim?' asked the old gentleman.

'Yes, he is, Mr Cheeryble,' replied the old clerk, looking at Nicholas over the top of his glasses.

Mr Cheeryble led Nicholas into another office. Nicholas couldn't believe his eyes when he saw Mr Cheeryble's brother – the two gentlemen looked exactly the same!

'Brother Ned, I'd like you to meet a young friend of mine who needs our help.'

'What does he need, Brother Charles?' the other man asked, looking at Nicholas with a kind smile.

Charles told his brother the details of Nicholas's situation and, after a long conversation, Ned went next door to speak to the old clerk, Tim Linkinwater. When he returned, he brought Tim Linkinwater with him.

'We've decided,' Ned told Nicholas, 'that you can work in the counting-house with Mr Linkinwater. Would you like that?'

Nicholas's eyes filled with tears of happiness. He did not know what to say.

'No, no, not a word now,' Charles said as Nicholas tried to thank him. 'You must return home. Your mother and sister will be worried about you. After we have checked a few details about you, Tim Linkinwater will visit you tonight.'

Nicholas returned home and told everybody his good news. That evening, Tim Linkinwater arrived and invited Nicholas to start work the next morning.

'The brothers will pay you 120 pounds a year,' Tim informed him. 'In addition to this, you and your family are welcome to move into a small cottage that belongs to them. It's not far from the office, the rent is very low, and they will also lend you the money to buy furniture.'

One week later, Mrs Nickleby, Kate, Smike and Nicholas moved into their new home.

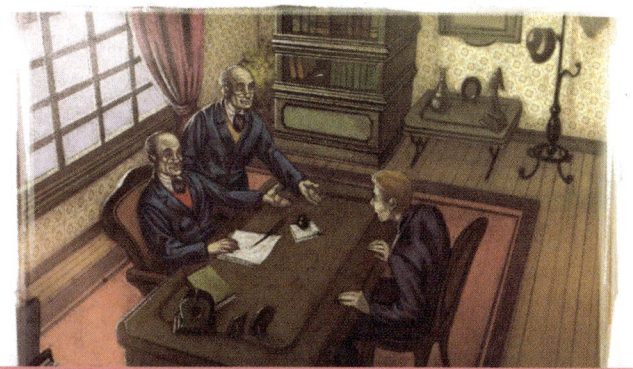

Before you read

1 Match the words in bold in sentences 1–4 with definitions a–d.
1 The **yard** was empty and dirty. ☐
2 Mr Griffin, the accountant, works in the **counting-house**. ☐
3 My dad works as a **clerk** in a bank. ☐
4 Last summer we stayed in a beautiful **cottage** near the forest. ☐

a someone who works in an office and keeps records or accounts
b an enclosed, outside area next to a building or group of buildings
c a small house, usually in the countryside
d an old name for the part of a building where financial records were kept

2 Look at the book cover and read the blurb. What do you think happens in the story?

While you read

3 🔊 RT2.1 Read and listen to the story and choose the correct option.
1 Nicholas meets *Uncle Ralph / an old man* in the street.
2 Nicholas *is looking / isn't looking* for a job.
3 *Uncle Ralph / The old man* helps Nicholas find a job.
4 Nicholas's family get a new *business / place to live*.

4 Read the story again and mark the sentences T (true) or F (false).
1 ☐ Charles Cheeryble is surprised that Nicholas is looking for work.
2 ☐ Nicholas tells Mr Cheeryble all about Uncle Ralph.
3 ☐ The Cheeryble brothers look very similar.
4 ☐ Nicholas is very happy when he is offered a job.
5 ☐ Tim offers Nicholas his cottage for the family to live in.
6 ☐ Nicholas and his family will be given furniture for the cottage.

After you read

5 Complete the sentences with words formed from the words in brackets. Then find the words in the story and check your answers.
1 I saw an _____ (advertise) online for the pet-walking job.
2 In _____ (add), you need to complete your hours on this form before you are paid.
3 I have a great boss – she's very _____ (kindness).
4 Don't worry, it's _____ (nature) to be nervous on your first day in a new job.

6 Complete the text with prepositions. Look at the words in bold to help you. Then find the words in bold in the story and check your answers.

Last year we **moved** ¹_____ a new area and I started a new weekend job at a supermarket. I was lucky as the supermarket was not **far** ²_____ our house. Before I started the job, we had a training day. The manager met us at the entrance and **led** us ³_____ the training room to **tell** us all ⁴_____ the work. I put my bag down on a chair. The manager gave us our uniforms and reminded us to **bring** them ⁵_____ us on the first day. Then he asked us to do a role play. He went to sit down, but my bag was on his chair. What's worse, it was a shopping bag from another supermarket! I watched in horror as he sat on it, then jumped up, with the bag, and asked, 'Ahem … Who does this **belong** ⁶_____?'

7 **WRAP UP** Complete the information about the story.

Title: _____
Type: *love story / horror story / adventure story*
Main characters: _____
_____
_____
My opinion: ☆☆☆☆☆

69 Unit 6

Beyond words

7

VOCABULARY
Effective communication and body language | Word building: communication | The media | Advertising

GRAMMAR
The passive: Present Simple, Past Simple, Present Perfect, modal verbs | The passive with *will*

7.1 Vocabulary

Communication and body language

1 ● **WORD FRIENDS** Look at the pictures and complete the phrases with the verbs below.

| fold | lower | make | ~~nod~~ | point | raise |
| shrug | stand |

1 *nod* your head
2 _____ an eyebrow 
3 _____ your shoulders 
4 _____ your arms 
5 _____ up straight 
6 _____ your finger 
7 _____ eye contact 
8 _____ your voice 

2 ● Choose the correct option.
1 I speak quite good French, but I find it difficult to *follow* / *watch* a conversation in a big group.
2 It's important to *watch* / *look* someone in the eye when you're talking to them.
3 Stop staring out of the window and *give* / *pay* attention. This is important.
4 Please don't *raise* / *up* your voice. The baby's sleeping.
5 I know you don't think it's a good idea, but try to *make* / *have* an open mind about this.
6 I tried to speak to her, but she just *closed* / *folded* her arms and looked the other way.

3 ●● Complete the sentences with one word in each gap.
1 James, you're shaking your *head*. Do you disagree?
2 _____ me in the eye and tell me it wasn't you who said those things about me.
3 Always make eye _____ with the customer. It shows you are interested in them.
4 Lisa could tell I was surprised because I raised an _____.
5 Can you lower your _____, please? This is a library.
6 My sister sometimes finds it difficult to concentrate and pay _____ in class.
7 Please don't _____ your shoulders. Say, 'I don't know.'
8 In my culture, it's rude to _____ your finger at people.

Unit 7

4 ● Complete the sentences with the noun form of the verbs in brackets.

1 People from different cultures use different forms of non-verbal *communication* (communicate).
2 Fiona sometimes finds it difficult to read people's facial _____ (express).
3 We had an interesting _____ (discuss) in class today about different cultures.
4 For homework, I want you to write a _____ (describe) of your last holiday.
5 I use a great app to help me with my _____ (pronounce) of new words in English.
6 Check in the dictionary for the correct _____ (define) of this word.
7 What shall we get Janine for her birthday? Do you have any _____ (suggest)?
8 Do you have any _____ (explain) for the way you behaved?
9 This book has lots of useful _____ (inform) about how to communicate.

5 ●●● Read the text and choose the correct answer.

1 a ⓐ communicate   b communication
   c discuss   d discussion
2 a speak   b pronounce
   c pronunciation   d repetition
3 a information   b descriptions
   c definitions   d expressions
4 a mouth   b eye
   c face   d head
5 a nodding   b raising
   c pointing   d moving
6 a head   b gestures
   c body   d voice
7 a suggest   b suggestion
   c definition   d define
8 a shake   b lower
   c shrug   d bow
9 a point   b shake
   c shrug   d lower
10 a body   b hand
   c head   d finger

Getting by in a foreign country

When I travel to another country, I always try to learn the language so I can ¹____ with local people. I don't just study words and grammar but ²____ too, so people can understand me. However, this isn't always possible, especially if you're just going somewhere for a short holiday. It's amazing how much you can express with gestures and facial ³____.

Looking somebody in the ⁴____ and ⁵____ your head is important because it shows you're paying attention to what they say. If you don't understand someone, stay calm and don't raise your ⁶____. There are better ways to show you don't understand. One ⁷____ is to simply ⁸____ your shoulders in a friendly way and smile.

Be careful with some gestures, though, as they can mean different things around the world. If you ⁹____ your head in Bulgaria, it actually means 'yes'. And in some countries, it's rude to point a ¹⁰____ at anything, especially other people.

I can talk about effective communication and body language.

7.2 Grammar
The passive

GRAMMAR — The passive

Present Simple
The game **is designed** for groups of 2–6.
Prizes **are given out** to the winners at the end.

Past Simple
The game **was created** by experts.
We **were invited** to an escape room recently.

Present Perfect
This new room **has** already **been visited** by hundreds of players.
Thousands of customers **have been challenged** by their games.

Modal verbs
The game **must be finished** in one hour.
It **can't be won** without teamwork.
Everyone **should be heard**.

1 ● Complete the sentences with the passive form of the verbs in brackets.
1 Billions of emails *are sent* every day. (send – Present Simple)
2 Mobile phones _____ for years. (use – Present Perfect)
3 The message _____ by Adam. (not write – Past Simple)
4 Mobile phones _____ in class. (turn off – must)
5 Ball games _____ here. (play – can't)
6 My stolen bike _____ yet. (not find – Present Perfect)

2 ●● Choose the correct option.

Last Tuesday, our class ¹(was sent)/ has been sent to a workshop on improving our communication skills. We were told ² by / for our teachers that it would be fun. They were right! We played several games in pairs and small groups. These are special games – they ³ can be designed / have been designed to make us communicate without speaking. They must ⁴ be played / been played using gestures or body language only. At the end we ⁵ have been asked / were asked what we thought of the workshop, and I gave it 10/10.]. I like it when we ⁶ were given / are given workshops like this at school. It makes the day much more interesting!

3 ●● Rewrite the sentences in the passive.
1 They speak English in India.
   English is spoken in India.
2 They make many mobile phones in China.
   _____
3 They haven't taught Latin in our school for years.
   _____
4 You can show your pictures on the big screen.
   _____
5 You must write your answers on this form.
   _____
6 They haven't made any good films this year.
   _____

4 ●●● Complete the article with the passive form of the verbs in brackets.

Teaching communication skills

What ¹*can be done* (can/do) to teach communication skills in school? The question ² _____ (answer) by one school in the north of England. At St Andrew's School, teachers believe that students ³ _____ (must/teach) how to communicate properly. They have special classes where students ⁴ _____ (show) how to introduce themselves, how to give presentations and the importance of eye contact. These classes started last year, when teachers noticed some students were having difficulties in speaking exams. Marks ⁵ _____ (lose) in exams because of communication problems.
Since then, a number of additional workshops ⁶ _____ (design) to help students practise these communication skills. One of the activities the pupils ⁷ _____ (give) is to prepare a short presentation. Students ⁸ _____ (record) by their partner using a mobile phone. The phones ⁹ _____ (swap) and they give each other feedback. Students find it useful when they get feedback from another student, rather than the teacher or the whole class, because it creates a 'safe' environment.

I can use verbs in the passive.

On the Portal
Extra Practice Activities: Lesson 7.2

7.3 Reading and Vocabulary
Honest or dishonest?

1 Match words/phrases 1–12 with definitions a–l.

1	d	listener	7		radio station
2		report (v)	8		reliable source
3		print (v)	9		on location
4		the media	10		viewer
5		audience	11		journalist
6		TV channel	12		the press

a publish something, e.g. in a newspaper
b a television company and the programmes it shows
c a person, book, document, etc. that provides you with information that you can trust to be true
d ~~someone who listens to a radio programme or podcast~~
e people who watch or listen to a particular programme or performance
f in the place where something is happening
g a radio company and the programmes it plays
h all the different ways of giving news and information to the public
i newspapers and magazines
j someone who writes news stories for newspapers, news sites, magazines, etc.
k give people information about events
l someone who watches television

2 Read the article quickly and put these things in the order they are mentioned.

a ☐ the face   c ☐ eye contact
b ☐ verbal signs   d ☐ gestures

3 Read the article again. For each gap (1–5), choose the correct sentence (a–g). There are two extra sentences. Listen and check.

a They're not really focusing on what they're doing with their hands.
b This is one of the hardest things to do when lying.
c For example, in some cultures, making eye contact is important for people to trust you.
d It may also be a sign that they're thinking hard about what to say next.
e In fact, the face may display several signs of dishonesty.
f Excessive use of fillers like 'uh', 'um' and 'like' is another verbal sign.
g Pay attention to what they do next.

I can understand an article about how to tell if someone is lying.

How to spot a liar

How can we tell if someone is lying or telling the truth? Whether you're a viewer watching a politician talking to a journalist or you're talking to someone you know, there are certain tell-tale signs that can help you decide if someone is telling the truth or lying. Here we explain some of them.

First of all, there are the non-verbal signs of communication.[1]____ But when someone is lying, they may do this too much or for too long. If someone is staring at you too intensely while they say something, this may be because they're lying and trying too hard to convince you they're telling the truth. [2]____

[3]____ Someone who is lying may look hot and you'll be able to see sweat on their face. They will also touch their face a lot, and even cover their mouth without thinking. Other types of 'closed' gestures, such as folding their arms or crossing their legs, can be another sign of lying.

Gestures have a lot to do with lying, and especially important is when people make hand gestures. If someone makes hand gestures after they've finished speaking, it's because their mind is busy thinking about what to say next. [4]____ Using both hands in gestures or even hiding their hands in their pockets or under the table is another sure sign.

There are also verbal signs which can help viewers tell if someone they're watching is lying. If the speaker suddenly raises their voice or speaks in a higher voice, they're probably lying. The same is true if they use a lot of phrases like 'honestly' or 'to tell you the truth'. [5]____

So whether verbal or non-verbal, there are a lot of ways people give the truth away, even when they're trying hard not to.

7.4 Grammar

The passive with *will*

> **GRAMMAR** — The passive with *will*
>
> The classes **will be aimed** at beginners.
> You **won't be expected** to do homework.
> **Will** we **be given** homework?

1 ● Complete the sentences with *will* and the passive form of the verbs in brackets.

1. Important information about the workshop *will be sent* (send) by email next week.
2. Careers advice _____ (give) during the workshop.
3. You _____ (teach) how to improve your communication skills.
4. Computers and mobile phones _____ (not allow) during the workshop.
5. A question and answer session _____ (hold) at the end.
6. You _____ (not test) during the workshop at all.

2 ●● Complete the sentences with *will* and the passive form of the verbs below.

| give | not offer | not use | send | ~~show~~ | win |

1. Students *will be shown* how to apply for college.
2. The writing competition _____ by the person who writes the best story.
3. These extra communication classes _____ to all students – only those who have failed speaking exams.
4. You _____ a text message with an access code. Use this to change your password on the website.
5. Peanuts _____ in this recipe as some people may have a food allergy.
6. A prize _____ for the best presentation.

3 ●●● Complete the text with *will* and the passive form of the verbs below. There are two extra verbs.

| ask | ~~choose~~ | discuss | give | organise | publish | read |

New student president

Next month a new student president [1]*will be chosen* by you, the students. Anyone who wishes to be student president must write a short text about why they think they should be president. The texts [2]_____ by the teachers. After that, they [3]_____ in the school magazine for other students to read. On the day of the election, students [4]_____ a form to complete with the name of the candidate they want to choose. The winning candidate [5]_____ to give a short speech.
Good luck!

4 ●●● Read the signs and notices. Write sentences with *will* and the passive form of the verbs in brackets.

> We're sorry, but the shop won't be open tomorrow because we're redecorating.
> **COME BACK ON FRIDAY!**

1. (close) *The shop will be closed tomorrow.*

> **New courses!** We have a range of new courses for the next school year.

2. (offer) _____

> **Party on Friday 8 July!**
> Let's celebrate the end of the school year together!

3. (hold) _____

> **Class meeting – things to discuss**
> • new class president • school trip
> • GreenTime project

4. (discuss) Three _____

> **FX900 smartphone** – the wait is nearly over!
> **IN SHOPS FROM 3 SEPTEMBER.**

5. (sell) _____

On the Portal
Extra Practice Activities: Lesson 7.4

Unit 7 — I can use the future form of the passive.

7.5 Listening and Vocabulary
Advertising

1 Choose the correct option.
1. I hate it when I'm watching a film and it's interrupted every fifteen minutes by *billboards / commercials*.
2. Sam's got a part-time job giving out *leaflets / slogans* in the High Street.
3. Who is our target *audience / poster* for the product?
4. What's your favourite *brand / logo* of soft drink?
5. I'm not sure about the new *slogan / logo*. I think it looks old-fashioned.

2 Read the clues and complete the crossword.

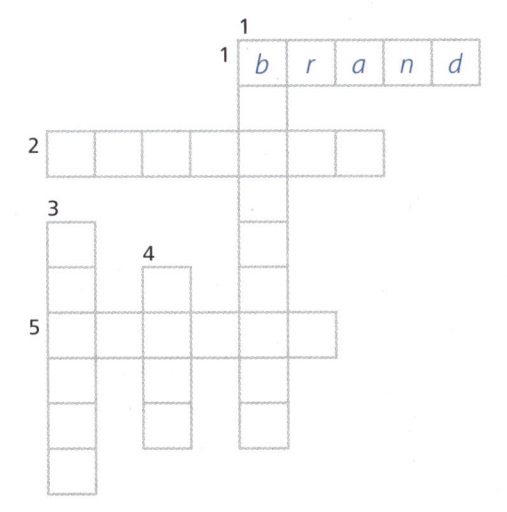

1 across: b r a n d

Across
1. the name of a particular kind of product made by one company
2. a piece of paper advertising an event or product
5. a short, easy-to-remember phrase used in advertisements

Down
1. a large sign outside which is used for advertising
3. a printed picture or photo advertising something which is put up in a public place
4. a small design or word which is the official sign of a company

3 🔊 **7.1** Listen to five extracts from TV commercials. Match commercials 1–5 with products A–H. There are three extra products.

A ☐ B ☐ C ☐ D ☐ E ☐ F ☐ G ☐ H ☐

4 🔊 **7.2** Listen to four short conversations. Choose the correct answer.
1. What time is Henry's garage sale?
   a six o'clock   b twelve o'clock
   c two o'clock
2. What does the football academy offer for free if you sign up for a summer course?
   a a T-shirt   b a football
   c football boots
3. What do you get free in the supermarket offer?
   a a plate   b a melon
   c two melons
4. Where is the new vegan restaurant?
   a a long way away   b on Green Lane
   c on the High Street

I can understand short TV commercials.

On the Portal
Extra Practice Activities: Lesson 7.5

75 Unit 7

7.6 Speaking
Clarifying and rephrasing

1 🔊 **7.3 Listen and repeat the phrases.**

SPEAKING — Clarifying and rephrasing

Asking for clarification
What do/did you mean?
Do/Did you mean this one?   Like this?
Are you saying/suggesting I should do it again?
When you say/said 'off-topic', what do/did you mean?
When you say/said 'off-topic', do/did you mean 'not related'?

Giving clarification
Sorry, I meant to say turn it on.   What I meant was turn it on.
What I am/was saying/trying to say is/was turn it on.
When I said another colour, I meant blue.
No, I don't/didn't mean to do it all again.
That's not what I mean/meant.

Rephrasing
In other words, keep it simple.
That's to say don't make it too difficult.
Let me put it another way.

2 Match the sentence halves.
1. [e] In other
2. [ ] What
3. [ ] Let me
4. [ ] Like
5. [ ] What I was trying
6. [ ] When you said 'LOL',

a this?
b what did you mean?
c do you mean?
d to say was that they're not popular these days.
e ~~words, make sure you're prepared.~~
f put it another way.

3 Order the words to make sentences.
1. mean / left / did / you / ?
   Did you mean left?
2. said / meant / green, / blue / I / I / when / !
   _____
3. suggesting / we / are / don't / it / do / you / ?
   _____
4. meant / not / that's / I / what
   _____
5. meant / sorry, / I / say / right / to
   _____

4 Complete the dialogues with question tags.
1. A: Did you like the film?
   B: Yes, it was good, *wasn't it*?
2. A: You don't like cheese, _____?
   B: No, I hate it!
3. A: Are you looking for Chiara?
   B: Yes, I am. You haven't seen her, _____?
4. A: I love running.
   B: Oh yes, you ran in a race last week, _____?
5. A: Harry never does his homework, _____?
   B: I know. I think he's going to fail the exam.

5 🔊 **7.4 Complete the dialogue with one word in each gap. Listen and check.**

Sam: Hey, Ellie, can you help me?
Ellie: Sure, what's up?
Sam: I've got to give a presentation in Science tomorrow, and …
Ellie: … And you want me to do your homework for you, don't you?
Sam: No, that's ¹*not* what I mean. What I was ²_____ to say was that I have all the information, but I'm just not good with the presentation software. My slides don't look very good.
Ellie: Ah, I see, sorry. Yes, I can help you with that. So the first thing you need is a good image for the title slide.
Sam: ³_____ this?
Ellie: Hmm … not really. ⁴_____ I meant was something connected to the topic of the presentation.
Sam: Well, the presentation is on the life cycle of plants. So are you ⁵_____ a nice image of a plant or flower would be good?
Ellie: Yes, or something with circles in it.
Sam: What do you ⁶_____?
Ellie: Let me ⁷_____ it another way. The topic is the life cycle of plants, so circles could represent that in a sort of abstract way. In ⁸_____ words, it's still connected to the topic, but not directly.
Sam: Ah right, good idea.

Unit 7 — I can ask for and give clarification and rephrase what I say.

On the Portal
Extra Practice Activities: Lesson 7.6

7.7 Writing
A review

1 Choose the correct option.
1. Oh no, I wrote in pen *by* / *on* mistake!
2. Look, these shoes are *in* / *on* sale. They're very cheap.
3. I did nothing *at* / *by* all at the weekend – just relaxed.
4. Sorry, I can't speak now. I'm *on* / *in* a hurry.
5. We waited ages for a bus but none came, so *at* / *in* the end, we just walked home.

2 Read the review quickly. Is it a positive or negative review overall?

Phonix: the new pronunciation app

There are hundreds of apps out there for language learning, so how can we know which ones are good? ¹*Lots of people have asked me about* Phonix, the pronunciation app, so I decided to write a review.

² _____ how easy it is to use. I was playing with it seconds after I'd downloaded it. ³ _____ by the games on it too. Some of them are fantastic and really fun to play. I could play them for hours!

⁴ _____, the design is a bit disappointing. The screens are quite boring and there aren't many pictures.

⁵ _____ it's an impressive app. If you don't mind the awful design, then it's worth the money. ⁶ _____ language learners.

3 Complete the review with phrases a–f.
a I was impressed
b I would definitely recommend it to
c All in all, I think
d ~~Lots of people have asked me about~~
e Unfortunately
f I particularly like

4 Put the information in the order it appears in the review.
a ☐ Say what you like and don't like.
b ☐ Give your personal opinion and recommendation.
c ☐ Say what you are reviewing and why you chose to review it.

5 Complete the notes about an app with the words below.

> confusing   design   remembering   sounds   useful   ~~vocabulary~~

XZLexis app
Type of app: ¹*vocabulary* recorder

What I liked:
- fantastic ² _____ – very beautiful
- fun games
- very ³ _____ for learning and ⁴ _____ vocabulary

What I didn't like:
- ⁵ _____ to use at times; instructions aren't clear
- ⁶ _____ and music on it are awful

Recommend it? Yes!

WRITING TIME

6 Write a review of an app. Use the ideas in Exercise 5 or your own.

1 Find ideas
Make notes about:
- what you are reviewing and why you are reviewing it.
- its advantages and disadvantages.
- your personal opinion and whether you would recommend it.

2 Plan and write
- Organise your ideas into paragraphs. Use the review in Exercise 2 to help you.
- Write a draft of your review.

3 Check
- Check language: have you included prepositional phrases?
- Check grammar: have you used the passive correctly?
- Write the final version of your review.

I can write a review and offer opinions and points of view.

My Language File

WORDLIST 🔊 7.5

Word friends
(effective communication and body language)

fold your arms _____
follow a conversation _____
have an open mind _____
look someone in the eye _____
lower your voice _____
make eye contact _____
nod your head _____
pay attention _____
point your finger _____
raise an eyebrow _____
raise your voice _____
shake your head _____
shrug your shoulders _____
stand up straight _____

Word building
(communication)

communicate (v) _____
communication (n) _____
define (v) _____
definition (n) _____
describe (v) _____
description (n) _____
discuss (v) _____
discussion (n) _____
explain (v) _____
explanation (n) _____
express (v) _____
expression (n) _____
inform (v) _____
information (n) _____
pronounce (v) _____
pronunciation (n) _____

suggest (v) _____
suggestion (n) _____

The media

audience (n) _____
journalist (n) _____
listener (n) _____
on location _____
print (v) _____
radio station (n) _____
reliable source _____
report (v) _____
reporter (n) _____
the press (n) _____
TV channel (n) _____
viewer (n) _____

Advertising

billboard (n) _____
brand (n) _____
commercial (n) _____
leaflet (n) _____
logo (n) _____
poster (n) _____
slogan (n) _____
target audience (n) _____

Extra words

accent (n) _____
advert (n) _____
April Fool's joke (n) _____
argument (n) _____
change the topic _____
chat (v) _____
communication skills (n) _____
complex (adj) _____
design (n) _____

emotional (adj) _____
graphics (n) _____
hilarious (adj) _____
humour (n) _____
ignore (v) _____
instruction (n) _____
left-handed (adj) _____
loudly (adv) _____
meaning (n) _____
news organisation (n) _____
observe (v) _____
play a trick _____
podcast (n) _____
politely (adv) _____
reason (n) _____
record (v) _____
role play (v) _____
rude (adj) _____
share ideas _____
shocked (adj) _____
shout (v) _____
sign language (n) _____
sit forward _____
sound quality (n) _____
speak clearly _____
speech (n) _____
tell a joke _____
tell lies _____
trust (v) _____
volume (n) _____
warning (n) _____
write an article _____

Sounds good!

Go on then! _____
OK, I get it! _____

MY LANGUAGE NOTES

My favourite words/expressions from this unit

Self-check

Vocabulary

1 Choose the correct option.
1 Have you seen that huge *billboard / slogan* in the High Street?
2 In your interview, make *look / eye* contact with the interviewer.
3 I find it difficult to *follow / read* a conversation if it's really boring.
4 Have you seen this *slogan / leaflet* I got in the music shop?
5 I know it sounds strange, but I like watching *logos / commercials*.
6 Don't raise your *eye / voice* at me!

2 Complete the sentences with the noun form of the verbs below.

> communicate   define   describe   discuss
> explain   inform   pronounce   suggest

1 You need to work on your _____ – how you say some words.
2 Look in the dictionary for a clear _____ of the word.
3 I always use the internet to look up _____ that I need.
4 He gave such a clear _____ of the place that it felt like we were there!
5 We need to have a _____ about your school work.
6 That's a great _____. Let's do that.
7 At school we have special classes to improve our _____ skills.
8 I don't understand what you mean. Can you give a simpler _____?

3 Match verbs 1–6 with words/phrases a–f.

1 ☐ shrug   a your head
2 ☐ stand   b up straight
3 ☐ pay   c your shoulders
4 ☐ shake   d your finger
5 ☐ fold   e attention
6 ☐ point   f your arms

Grammar

4 Rewrite the sentences in the passive. Use *by* if necessary.
1 Our Maths teacher gave us lots of homework.
We _____.
2 They play football in Brazil.
Football _____.
3 They have advertised their new product on billboards.
Their new product _____.
4 You must follow the rules at all times.
The rules _____.
5 You can't take photos in here.
Photos _____.
6 Flyby has announced a new flight to Ireland.
A new flight to Ireland _____.
7 Someone told me it was OK.
I _____.
8 They have created a new company website.
A new company website _____.

5 Complete the text with *will* and the passive form of the verbs in brackets.

The government has announced that 100 new technical schools ¹_____ (open) across the country. A range of modern courses ²_____ (offer) by each school, such as Computer Programming and Communication Skills. Also, students ³_____ (teach) how to drive by qualified driving instructors, and basic car repairs ⁴_____ (include) in the course too. The schools ⁵_____ (build) using recyclable materials and they ⁶_____ (locate) in poorer areas of the country, where it is hoped that education standards ⁷_____ (improve).

Speaking

6 Complete the dialogues with one word in each gap.
1 A: _____ you texted 'TTYL', what did you mean?
   B: What I was trying to _____ was 'Talk To You Later.'
2 A: _____ you suggesting I throw it away?
   B: No, that's not _____ I meant. I meant improve it. That's to _____ repaint it or something.

YOUR SCORE

Vocabulary: __/20   Speaking: __/5
Grammar: __/15   Total: __/40

Experience art

8

VOCABULARY
Visual arts | Describing art | Literature and books | Painting | Journalism

GRAMMAR
Modal verbs for ability | Modal verbs for obligation and prohibition

8.1 Vocabulary
Art and literature

1 ● Write the words below in the correct column. Then label photos A–F with six of the words.

> ~~abstract art~~   architecture   art installation   classic art
> design   film-making   impressionist art   modern art
> photography   pop art   sculpture

Styles of painting	Art forms
abstract art	

A. _art installation_
B. _____
C. _____
D. _____
E. _____
F. _____

2 ●● Choose the correct option.
1. I love the (design) / architecture of this website. It looks really good.
2. I really like how impressionist / modern art shows the light in different ways.
3. There are several art installations / sculptures hidden around the park.
4. I first got into modern art / photography when my parents bought me a camera.
5. I don't really like modern / classic art. I much prefer the very old stuff.

3 ● Match the words below with the definitions. There is one extra word.

> author   autobiography   chapter   character   cover
> ~~non-fiction~~   novelist   plot   title

1. a book which describes facts: _non-fiction_
2. a book someone writes about their life: _____
3. the story of a book, play or film: _____
4. a person in a book, play or film: _____
5. a section of a book: _____
6. a person who writes long stories: _____
7. the name of a book: _____
8. a person who writes a book: _____

4 ●● Complete the words in the sentences.

1. I love the characters in this book, but the p l o t is a bit boring.
2. I prefer reading n__n-f_____n books to f_____n. I like to read about things which actually happened.
3. I sometimes decide to buy a book because I like the image on the c_____r.
4. Who was the a_____r of *War and Peace*?
5. I'm reading a great crime n_____l at the moment.
6. I often like to read a s_____t s_____y when I don't have time to read a whole book.
7. Have you read the b_____y of J.K. Rowling? She's had a very interesting life.
8. What's the t_____e of the book you're reading at school?

5 ● **WORD FRIENDS** Match verbs 1–8 with phrases a–h.

1. [b] have — a a piece of music
2. [ ] visit — b a mysterious atmosphere
3. [ ] paint — c a powerful work of art
4. [ ] create — d bright colours
5. [ ] use — e a book
6. [ ] publish — f an art exhibition
7. [ ] perform — g an unusual building
8. [ ] design — h a portrait

6 ●● Complete the sentences with the words below. There are two extra words.

| atmosphere building colour dance exhibition |
| landscape poems work |

1. Can you suggest somewhere local where I can paint a *landscape* for my art project?
2. I love how this picture creates a warm _____ in this room, especially in winter.
3. Some of my friends performed a _____ in front of the school today. It was pretty cool.
4. Alicia created an unusual _____ of art in Art class today. It was very abstract.
5. Did you know Nish's dad has published some _____ in a book?
6. Last weekend, I visited an art _____ at the National Portrait gallery.

7 ●●● Choose the correct option.

The Upside Down Man

This weekend, I was lucky enough to visit an art ¹*installation* / (*exhibition*) / *plot* at the National Museum of Contemporary Art. There were several paintings, but also many interesting art ²*installations* / *landscapes* / *scenes*. One of these was called The Upside Down Man. It was a giant ³*landscape* / *exhibition* / *sculpture* of a man hanging upside down in the main hall. As soon as you walked in, you could feel the mysterious ⁴*atmosphere* / *building* / *portrait* that it created around the whole hall. The exhibition also featured a work by new artist Kelly Davroe, the ⁵*character* / *novelist* / *author* of several non-⁶*biography* / *fiction* / *plot* books about art.

I can talk about works of art and books.

8.2 Grammar
Modal verbs for ability

GRAMMAR — Modal verbs for ability

Present
She *can*/*can't* paint.
They*'re able to*/*aren't able to* read quickly.

Past
I *could*/*couldn't* follow the plot.
Jack *was*/*wasn't able to* go to the library.
He *managed*/*didn't manage to* read the book in a day.

Future
I*'ll be*/*won't be able to* finish this today.

Questions
Can/*Could* he paint?   No, he *can't*/*couldn't*.
Is/*Was* she able to read quickly?   Yes, she *is*/*was*.
Will you *be able to* read more books?   No, I *won't*.
Did he *manage to* finish the book?   Yes, he *did*.

Use
We use *could* to describe general ability in the past.
We use *managed to* to describe specific achievements in the past.

1 ● Match the sentence halves.
1 [c] I couldn't
2 [ ] Sheila can
3 [ ] Unfortunately, Keith won't
4 [ ] Will you be able
5 [ ] We can't
6 [ ] I managed

a read in five languages!
b offer you a place at our college, I'm afraid.
c ~~understand the French film – they all spoke very fast.~~
d to find the book you wanted.
e to finish the book this week?
f be able to come to the party.

2 ● Choose the correct option.
1 (Were) / Did you able to ride a bike when you were five?
2 Ben and Eve won't *be able* / *able* to come to the play.
3 Can you *write* / *to write* poetry?
4 I managed *to read* / *reading* fifteen books over the summer!
5 The theatre was so full of people that I *couldn't* / *could* see the stage.
6 I started writing a novel, but I didn't *manage* / *manage to* finish it.

3 ●● Choose the word or phrase which does NOT fit each sentence.
1 ____ to speak to your mum last night?
  a Did you manage   b Were you able
  (c) Could you
2 I ____ post that package for you – sorry.
  a can't   b managed to
  c won't be able to
3 I ____ read when I was three, but only slowly.
  a can   b could
  c was able to
4 I ____ drive, but I'm taking lessons.
  a can't   b 'm not able to
  c managed to
5 The book was difficult to follow, but I ____ finish it.
  a couldn't   b was able to
  c managed to

4 ●●● Complete the text with one word in each gap.

Thank you, Ms Palmer!

When I was younger, I wasn't very good at anything. I couldn't swim, I wasn't ¹*able* to read very well and I ²_____n't ride a bike on my own until I was twelve! People used to ask me things like, '³_____ you say "thank you" in French?' and I just looked down and felt embarrassed. The problem was I just didn't have any confidence. I ⁴_____ able to do these things if I really tried, but I didn't believe I could.

Then a new French teacher came to our school. Her name was Ms Palmer and she gave me lots of attention. She really encouraged me and said things like, 'If you ⁵_____ to read this text, I'll let you play that French game on your tablet for ten minutes.' It worked, and not only did my French improve, but now I ⁶_____ able to do lots of other things and I feel more confident too. Next year, I'm hoping I will ⁷_____ able to learn Spanish and Italian too. Merci beaucoup, Ms Palmer!

8.3 Reading and Vocabulary
A young artist

1 Complete the sentences with the words below.

> blocks   canvas   display   image   gallery
> self   simple   ~~typical~~

1. The artist's new piece was a change in direction, as it wasn't her *typical* style.
2. This music always creates a(n) _____ of a dark landscape in my mind.
3. It's incredible how you've created this picture just using _____ lines.
4. Have you ever painted a(n) _____-portrait?
5. Banksy's new work is on _____ at the Tate Modern at the moment.
6. I usually paint on _____, but sometimes I paint on paper.
7. We visited an interesting art _____ when we went to London.
8. She usually paints using _____ of colour to create abstract art.

2 Read the article quickly. Where does Aelita get her ideas for painting?

3 Read the article again and answer the questions.

1. How old was Aelita when she painted her first picture?
2. What did her dad think about her first picture?
3. What did the people at the Melbourne art gallery want to do when they saw her work?
4. How long did it take to sell all the tickets for the New York exhibition?
5. What unusual objects does she sometimes include in her paintings?
6. What do people watch her do at her live events?

'An artist before she could talk'

Aelita Andre is a young Australian painter, but she is not your average artist. When she was just nine months old, her dad, who used to paint occasionally, put out some canvas and began to paint. Then Aelita sat on the canvas and started using her hands, feet and legs to move the paint around. Her father could see how happy she was, but when he stood up and looked at the image, he was really surprised – it was amazing and very beautiful.

Her parents were so impressed with her work that they took it to a major art gallery in Melbourne, looking for a professional opinion. The people at the gallery liked the painting so much that they wanted to put her work on display. Aelita was one year old at that time. Her art became more popular and she had her first solo exhibition in Australia at the age of two. By 2011, she was known internationally, and her exhibition at the Agora Art Gallery in New York was so popular that it sold out in just seven days.

Her typical style is abstract, and varies from simple lines to big blocks of colour. She often includes real toys in her pictures, stuck to the canvas. Many art experts consider her work to be brilliant.

She has travelled the world, putting her work on display at art galleries and even doing 'live painting' events where people come to see her in action. People may think that such success at an early age could be difficult for her, but she leads a very normal life otherwise. She plays the piano and violin, and likes ballet and gymnastics. She also loves animals. At home they have chickens, a rabbit, guinea pigs, a turtle and some fish. She says she gets a lot of her ideas about what to paint from nature: trees, animals and space. Let's hope we get to see a lot more of her beautiful work in the future.

I can understand an article about a young artist.

8.4 Grammar

Modal verbs for obligation and prohibition

> **GRAMMAR** — **Modal verbs for obligation and prohibition**
>
> **Obligation**
> You **must**/**have to** read.
> They **had to** read.
> I **will have to** read.
> **Do**/**Did**/**Will** you **have to** read?
> Yes, I **do**/**did**/**will**.
>
> **Lack of obligation**
> You **don't have to** come.
> He **won't have to** come.
> She **didn't have to** come.
>
> **Prohibition**
> You **can't** go.
> You **mustn't**/**aren't allowed to** go.
> I **wasn't allowed to** go.
> He **won't be allowed to** go.
> **Are**/**Were** you **allowed to** stay late?
> **Will** you **be allowed to** stay late?
>
> *Must* and *mustn't* don't have past or future forms. We use *had to* or *will have to* instead. In question forms, we usually use *have to*.

1 ● Decide if the meanings of the sentences are similar (S) or different (D).

1. You must do your homework tonight.
   You have to do your homework tonight. **S**
2. Jake had to wear a shirt.
   Jake was allowed to wear a shirt. ☐
3. It's important that they don't leave any litter.
   They mustn't leave any litter. ☐
4. We won't have to pay for it.
   It won't be necessary for us to pay for it. ☐

2 ●● Complete the text with the words below.

> allowed   aren't   ~~don't~~   must   mustn't

There's an unusual exhibition on at the art gallery in town. You ¹*don't* have to pay anything, but you can if you want to. The exhibition is interesting because you are ² _____ to touch the pieces in the gallery. You can pick them up, throw them around, even break them! But you ³ _____ allowed to say bad things about them. At the end you can even write your opinion of the exhibition in a little book, but of course it ⁴ _____ be something positive. And you ⁵ _____ write more than three words. It's quite weird, but interesting, I think.

3 ●● Complete the second sentence with the word in bold so that it means the same as the first one. Use no more than five words.

1. I'll have to go to bed early tonight. **ALLOWED**
   I *won't be allowed* to stay up late tonight.
2. To do this activity, you have to ask three other students the questions. **MUST**
   To do this activity, you _____ three other students the questions.
3. They didn't have to leave. **WERE**
   They _____ stay.
4. You mustn't talk during the presentation. **ALLOWED**
   You _____ during the presentation.
5. Were you allowed to go out on your own when you were younger? **HAVE**
   _____ go out with an adult when you were younger?

4 ●●● Complete the blog post with one word in each gap.

A TALE OF TWO SCHOOLS

My last school was very unusual because there were almost no rules. We were ¹*allowed* to wear what we wanted (there was no uniform) and we did ² _____ have to do any homework. In fact, we didn't ³ _____ to go to class if we didn't want to! But we ⁴ _____ to respect each other and no fighting or bullying was allowed.

My new school is completely the opposite. We ⁵ _____ do all our homework and if we don't do it, we ⁶ _____ to do double homework as a punishment. We ⁷ _____ not allowed to wear anything we want – we have ⁸ _____ wear a school uniform. But they are thinking about changing this rule next year, so we won't have ⁹ _____ wear specific clothes. But we will still ¹⁰ _____ to dress in smart clothes – we won't ¹¹ _____ allowed to wear jeans and trainers, for example.

Unit 8 — 84 — I can talk about obligation and prohibition in the past, present and future.

On the Portal
Extra Practice Activities: Lesson 8.4

8.5 Listening and Vocabulary
A day as a newspaper journalist

1 Match the words below with the definitions.

> advert   celebrity gossip   editor   headline
> magazine   news app   ~~newspaper~~   paparazzi

1. a traditional way of reading the news: _newspaper_
2. news about famous people which may or may not be true: _____
3. a large but thin book which has stories and photos and is published every week or month: _____
4. the head of a newspaper or magazine who decides what stories are published: _____
5. the title of a newspaper report: _____
6. photographers who take photos of famous people to sell to newspapers: _____
7. something you use to read the news on your phone: _____
8. a short text which tries to sell you something: _____

2 Choose the correct option.
1. My aunt is a (designer) / journalist. She organises the look of the texts and photos on the page so it all looks good.
2. I never read the national / local news. It's always just stories about lost animals.
3. I usually read the celebrity gossip / headlines quickly first to decide which stories I want to read in more detail.
4. I don't buy newspapers any more. I just read the news in a magazine / on an online news site.
5. When you've finished writing the article, send it to our editor / reporter who decides what will be included in the latest issue of the magazine.
6. I need to check the adverts / weather forecast so I know what to wear tomorrow.

3 🔊 8.1 Listen to an interview with an editor, Naomi. Mark the sentences T (true) or F (false).
1. ☐ *The Rosedale Record* won a famous award recently.
2. ☐ The newspaper is written by experienced professional journalists.
3. ☐ At first, the school didn't mind what stories they wrote.
4. ☐ Naomi chose to print the story about the company.
5. ☐ They became a national newspaper with no help from anyone else.

4 🔊 8.1 Listen again and choose the correct answer.
1. *The Rosedale Record* is a
   a student magazine.   b school newspaper.
   c national newspaper.
2. Naomi thinks it's important to be
   a interesting.   b honest.
   c positive.
3. At first, the school wouldn't let them write about
   a things outside the school.
   b people in the school.
   c positive stories.
4. What type of story did Miguel have?
   a a positive one   b a negative one
   c a neutral one
5. How did the headteacher react to the story?
   a She let them publish it.
   b She asked them to rewrite it.
   c She stopped the newspaper.
6. Someone from another newspaper gave them
   a advice and materials.   b stories and money.
   c advice and money.

I can understand an interview about the press.

8.6 Speaking
Comparing ideas and expressing opinions

1 🔊 **8.2** Listen and repeat the phrases.

SPEAKING — Comparing ideas and expressing opinions

Comparing ideas
On the one hand, I liked the song, but on the other hand, it was a bit slow.
(Personally,) I think Sara's song is better/more interesting than Andrea's.
A barbecue is the best idea because the weather is nice.
It's exactly/almost the same as the first one.
A magazine is totally different from a newspaper.

Expressing opinions
In my opinion, pop music is brilliant/amazing/awful.
As I see it, this is the best option.   I think you're right.
As far as I can see, it isn't a new idea.
As far as I'm concerned, it isn't a new idea.
It seems to me that everybody likes it.
If you ask me, we should think of something different.
I'm not sure it's the best idea.
I could be wrong, but I don't think it will be very popular.

2 Choose the correct option.
1 If you *ask* / *tell* me, I think it's a bad idea.
2 In my *thinking* / *opinion*, it's amazing.
3 *Personally,* / *As far as I see it*, I think rap is more interesting than rock music.
4 I'm not *sure* / *know* which is best.
5 This magazine is exactly the same *as* / *to* the one I usually buy.

3 Complete the sentences with the words below. There are two extra words.

> ~~concerned~~   far   from   one   other   see   seems   wrong

1 As far as I'm *concerned*, it doesn't matter what we do.
2 I could be _____, but I think he's a teacher.
3 Paparazzi are totally different _____ other types of photographers.
4 It _____ to me that we're not looking at all the possibilities.
5 On the _____ hand, it doesn't taste as good, but on the _____ hand, it's much cheaper.

4 Choose the correct answer.
1 A buffet is the ___ idea for the party because everybody can find something they like.
   a good   **b best**   c worst
2 The problem, as ___ it, is that the book was boring, so the film won't be any better.
   a I see   b I think   c I'm concerned
3 If you ___ me, we should have the event on a Saturday.
   a tell   b see   c ask
4 As ___ as I can see, there's no reason not to write a rap song about snakes!
   a far   b long   c right
5 I think this film is ___ the same as the one we watched last week!
   a far   b exactly   c right

5 🔊 **8.3** Complete the dialogue with one word in each gap. Listen and check.

Tia: So, which song do you think should win the school talent contest, Rob?
Rob: What a difficult decision! In [1] *my* opinion, they're all really good.
Tia: I know, right? On the one [2] _____, I really like Lauren's song about her friend who moved away, but [3] _____ the other hand, Ollie's rap about his pet snake was funny!
Rob: Exactly. It seems to [4] _____ that we need to decide if we go for the emotional one or the funny one.
Tia: Well, [5] _____ I see it, Lauren's song is totally different from Ollie's. I don't [6] _____ Ollie is very musical, to be honest.
Rob: I see what you mean. I'm not [7] _____ which is better though.
Tia: I know. It's difficult to choose.
Rob: OK, well, if you [8] _____ me, I think we should choose Ollie's rap. It's funny and original.
Tia: I think you're [9] _____. Shall I tell him or do you want to?
Rob: You can if you want.

I can compare ideas and express opinions.

8.7 Writing
A comparison

1 Read the comparison and answer the questions.
1. How are the paintings similar?
   They both show London Bridge.
2. What is painted on the river in Picture A?
   _____
3. What is painted on the river in Picture B?
   _____
4. Which is the author's favourite painting?
   _____

A   B

A comparison of two paintings of London

Matt Gibson is a photographer and painter who specialises in nature and landscapes. I will compare two of his paintings. Although the paintings show the same view of Tower Bridge, Gibson manages to make each painting different. Both paintings depict sunrise in autumn, but with different weather conditions. The paintings are digital watercolours.

The first painting, A, is much darker than painting B. In A, you can see grey and dark blue colours, and heavy clouds, which represent a stormy day. You can also see the sunrise, which is represented by the colour gold. The reflection of the bridge and the sunrise are painted dramatically on the river.

Painting B, on the other hand, has got more white, and light grey and brown colours. It also uses the colour orange to represent the sunrise. Picture B is more peaceful, perhaps showing a foggy day. While picture A focuses on the bridge, picture B shows more buildings, a ship on the river and the bridge in the background.

I like both paintings, but on balance, I prefer B because it is more abstract and calmer. I also think the depiction of the sunrise is more beautiful.

2 Choose the correct option.
1. (*In spite of*) / *Even though* having a lot of colour, the painting isn't very attractive.
2. *Although / Despite* it is a modern painting, it looks very old.
3. *Despite / Even though* this is a great copy, I prefer the original version.
4. *Although / Despite* being a terrible novel, it is very popular.

3 Make notes on two paintings, for example, the original Mona Lisa and a modern version. Use these headings.

Paragraph 1: Introduction with background information
_____
_____

Paragraphs 2–3: Making comparisons
_____
_____
_____
_____

Paragraph 4: Conclusion and personal comment
_____
_____
_____

WRITING TIME

4 Write a comparison of two paintings. Use your notes from Exercise 3 to help you.

1 Find ideas
Think about:
- information for your introduction.
- a description of the two paintings, including similarities and differences.
- your conclusion about which you prefer and why.

2 Plan and write
- Organise your ideas into paragraphs. Use the comparison in Exercise 1 to help you.
- Write a draft of your comparison.

3 Check
- Check language: have you included linkers of contrast?
- Check grammar: have you used modal verbs for ability correctly?
- Write the final version of your comparison.

I can write a comparison of two works of art.

My Language File

WORDLIST 🔊 8.4

Visual arts
abstract art (n) _____
architecture (n) _____
art installation (n) _____
classic art (n) _____
design (n) _____
film-making (n) _____
impressionist art (n) _____
modern art (n) _____
photography (n) _____
pop art (n) _____
sculpture (n) _____

Word friends
(describing art)
choose bright/clear colours _____
create an impressive/a memorable/
  a powerful work of art _____
design a colourful/an unusual
  building _____
have a mysterious/unique/warm
  atmosphere _____
paint a landscape/portrait/
  scene _____
perform a dance/piece of
  music _____
publish a book/a newspaper/
  poems _____
use bright/clear colours _____
visit an art exhibition _____

Literature and books
author (n) _____
autobiography (n) _____
biography (n) _____
chapter (n) _____
character (n) _____
cover (n) _____
fiction (n) _____
non-fiction (n) _____
novel (n) _____
novelist (n) _____
plot (n) _____
short story (n) _____
title (n) _____

Painting
art gallery (n) _____
block of colour (n) _____
canvas (n) _____
image (n) _____
on display _____
self-portrait (n) _____
simple line (n) _____
typical style (n) _____
work (n) _____

Journalism
advert (n) _____
celebrity gossip (n) _____
designer (n) _____
editor (n) _____
headline (n) _____
journalist (n) _____
local news (n) _____
magazine (n) _____
national news (n) _____
news app (n) _____
newspaper (n) _____
online news site (n) _____
paparazzi (n) _____
reporter (n) _____
weather forecast (n) _____

Extra words
comic (n) _____
craft (n) _____
criticism (n) _____
do an interview with _____
express emotions _____
graphic novel (n) _____
impressionism (n) _____
inspiration (n) _____
light show (n) _____
microphone (n) _____
oil painting (n) _____
piece of art (n) _____
poet (n) _____
process (v) _____
rap artist (n) _____
read aloud _____
represent (v) _____
rhyme (v) _____
shape (n) _____
skilled (adj) _____
sound effects (n) _____
true story (n) _____
visual information (n) _____

Sounds good!
Are you kidding me? _____
This is a total disaster! _____

MY LANGUAGE NOTES

My favourite words/expressions from this unit

Self-check

Vocabulary

1 Choose the correct option.
1 Jana's really into *photography / sculpture*. She carries her camera everywhere.
2 Sit still and try not to move while I paint your *landscape / portrait*.
3 I rarely buy a newspaper any more – I just use my news *magazine / app*.
4 I'd love to be an *author / impressionist* and write books.
5 This is Gemma, our *novelist / designer*. She makes sure every page looks just right before we print.
6 Have you checked the *weather forecast / celebrity gossip*? You might need an umbrella.
7 When I'm in a hurry, I just read the *adverts / headlines* to find out what's happening in the news.
8 I couldn't follow the *plot / character* of that film – it was too complicated.

2 Write the correct word for each definition.
1 the outside of a book: c_ _ _ _ _
2 a book about someone's life, which someone else writes: b_ _ _ _ _ _ _ _ _
3 a book about real facts: n_ _ -f_ _ _ _ _ _
4 a person who writes a book: a_ _ _ _ _
5 a book with a fictional story: n_ _ _ _
6 a section of a book: c_ _ _ _ _ _

3 Complete the sentences with the words below. There are two extra words.

> choose   create   design   has   paint
> perform   published   visit

1 Caity is going to _____ a piece of music in the school concert.
2 I wanted to _____ a memorable work of art that people wouldn't forget.
3 Did you know Carla's mum has _____ a book?
4 I'd like to _____ a colourful building for the new library.
5 I really want to _____ the art exhibition on at the town hall at the moment.
6 This room _____ a warm atmosphere because of that big painting on the wall.

Grammar

4 Complete the sentences with the correct form of the words in brackets.
1 Sorry, I _____ (not able/call) you yesterday.
2 _____ (you/able/return) this book to the library tomorrow?
3 I _____ (cannot/swim) when I was four.
4 _____ (you/manage/finish) your painting last night?
5 They _____ (not able/go) on holiday next year.

5 Choose the correct option.
1 A: What do we *have to / must* do today?
   B: We *have / have to* tidy up.
2 A: *Did / Were* you allowed to stay up late when you were little?
   B: Oh no. I *had / have* to be in bed by 7 p.m.
3 A: Sorry, I'll have *to leave / leave* at 2 p.m.
   B: OK. You *didn't / won't* have to stay any longer.
4 A: *Is / Does* Jake allowed to visit us?
   B: Only if his mum says he *is allowed to / has to* come.
5 A: You *must / must to* buy a ticket before you get onto the bus.
   B: Oh, I *don't have to / 'm not allowed to* buy one. I have a monthly pass.

Speaking

6 Complete the dialogue with one word in each gap.

Liz: What's your favourite kind of art, Kai?
Kai: I'm not sure. [1]_____ the one hand, I like modern art, but on the [2]_____ hand, some classic art is just brilliant.
Liz: I know what you mean. [3]_____ my opinion, classical portraits are amazing …
Kai: Oh, I don't know. As I [4]_____ it, you just can't compare modern art and classic art.
Liz: Maybe. But as far as I'm [5]_____, modern art is strange.

YOUR SCORE

Vocabulary: __/20   Speaking: __/5
Grammar: __/15   Total: __/40

Party time!

VOCABULARY Celebrations | Special occasions | Types of celebrations | Phrases to express likes | Sense verbs

GRAMMAR Defining and non-defining clauses | Direct and indirect questions

9.1 Vocabulary
Celebrations

1 ● Match the words below with photos 1–5.

ceremony · costume · festival · firework display · parade

1 _costume_
2 _____
3 _____
4 _____
5 _____

2 ●● Choose the correct option.
1 Wow! I love your Spiderman *custom* / (*costume*)!
2 In Spain, it's a *tradition* / *parade* to eat twelve grapes on New Year's Eve.
3 Come out with us tonight. It's a special *display* / *occasion*: Maisie's birthday!
4 We stood by the side of the road and watched the *parade* / *festival* come past.
5 Are you going to the local food *occasion* / *festival* this year?

3 ● **WORD FRIENDS** Match verbs 1–10 with words/phrases a–j.
1 _e_ wrap   a a birthday
2 ☐ get together   b good luck
3 ☐ turn   c with friends
4 ☐ follow   d fireworks
5 ☐ celebrate   e ~~presents~~
6 ☐ put up   f decorations
7 ☐ throw   g eighteen
8 ☐ stay   h a party
9 ☐ light   i a tradition
10 ☐ bring   j up late

4 ●● Choose the correct option.
1 Do you follow the *costume* / (*tradition*) of lighting *fireworks* / *decorations* on Independence Day?
2 It's my friend's birthday today. I'm putting up *presents* / *decorations* and we're going to *throw* / *follow* her a surprise party.
3 I stayed *up* / *on* really late on the night of the festival.
4 This year I'm getting *together* / *up* with the whole family to celebrate my cousin *turning* / *staying* eighteen.
5 How do you want to *organise* / *celebrate* your birthday this year? Shall we *prepare* / *wrap* a big meal for the whole family? And I'll make a cake too!
6 Chris's birthday was great. After he *wrapped* / *unwrapped* his presents, we brought out a cake and he blew out the *candles* / *fireworks*.

Unit 9

5 ● Read the descriptions and complete the words for celebrations.

> When Angie walked in, we all came out and shouted, 'Happy Birthday!' She had no idea we were waiting there.

1 s_u_ _r_ _p_ _r_ _i_ _s_ _e_ p_a_ _r_ _t_ _y_

> We all wore different costumes – I was an avocado!

2 f_ _ _ _ -d_ _ _ _ _ p_ _ _ _ _

> After the last day of school, we put on smart clothes and danced in the school hall.

3 s_ _ _ _ _ _ _ p_ _ _ _

> After they got married, we had a big party in the community centre.

4 w_ _ _ _ _ _ _ r_ _ _ _ _ _ _ _ _

> At the end of the school year, the senior students wore smart clothes and ate together.

5 f_ _ _ _ _ _ _ d_ _ _ _ _ _

> All the family went to my gran's house on her eightieth birthday.

6 f_ _ _ _ _ _ g_ _ -t_ _ _ _ _ _ _

> We had a big party in the street and people wore costumes as part of the celebrations.

7 c_ _ _ _ _ _ _ _ _

6 ●● Complete the sentences with one word in each gap.

1 My sister had her wedding _reception_ in the local community centre.
2 Last weekend, I went to a _____-dress party in a Superman costume.
3 At the end of the year, Liam is taking his friend Ella to the school _____.
4 Last weekend, we had a big family _____ and I saw my uncle, who I hadn't seen for five years!
5 Last year, we had a big _____ party outside with all the neighbours, to celebrate the royal wedding.

I can talk about celebrations and special occasions.

7 ●●● Choose the correct option.

My Day

In our family, we ¹(*follow*)/ *prepare* a tradition which I don't think any other family has, called My Day. On 1 January, we have a family ²*come-together* / *get-together* and celebrate ³*turning* / *staying* a year older. We then each choose one day that year which will be our 'My Day', and we all make that day a really ⁴*formal* / *special* occasion. When someone's 'My Day' comes, we put up ⁵*fireworks* / *decorations* and say, 'Happy My Day!' to that person. We give them presents and a cake with candles. The person then ⁶*blows out* / *lights* the candles and ⁷*brings* / *unwraps* their presents. In the evening, we have a ⁸*surprise* / *formal* dinner for all the family and some friends, and afterwards we have a firework ⁹*display* / *reception* in the garden. We've done this for as long as I can remember and according to my dad, his family did it too. He thinks that if we ever missed a 'My Day', it would ¹⁰*bring* / *get* bad luck.

9.2 Grammar
Defining and non-defining relative clauses

GRAMMAR — Defining and non-defining relative clauses

Defining relative clauses explain which person, thing or place we are talking about. The sentence makes no sense without them.
There are some special festivals *that*/*which* are not as well-known.
This takes place in countries *where* it's very cold.

Non-defining relative clauses give extra information about the person, thing or place we are talking about. The sentence makes sense without them.
I'm joined by Zac, *who* has been finding out about some special festivals.
Mel, *whose* podcast is quite popular, has a lovely voice.

1 ● Complete the sentences with *who*, *which*, *where* or *whose*. Then mark the relative clauses defining (D) or non-defining (ND).

1. That's the street *where* the parade will take place. *D*
2. That's the girl _____ costume won a prize. ____
3. The present, _____ we bought for Clara, was made by hand. ____
4. The DJ, _____ music collection was all from the 1990s, wasn't very popular. ____
5. That's the restaurant _____ I had my birthday dinner. ____
6. The spectators, _____ were clearly having a good time, made lots of noise. ____

2 ●● Complete the text with one relative pronoun in each gap.

I can't wait until next Friday. It's our last day at school and in the evening we're having a big leaving party with our teachers. This week I bought the jacket ¹*which* I'll wear to the party. I've been looking at it in the shop window for ages! The shop assistant, ² _____ knew I wanted it, kept it to the side for me. The jacket, ³ _____ is made by hand, is really cool and fits me really well! The place ⁴ _____ the party is will be decorated nicely. At the party, the principal of the school, ⁵ _____ daughter is also leaving, will make a toast to us for the future and then we'll dance, dance, dance!

3 ●● Complete the sentences with relative clauses. Use the correct relative pronouns and the words in brackets.

1. The hall, *which we hired for the prom* (we hired it for the prom), was very nice.
2. Teachers _____ (they give lots of homework for the weekend) aren't usually very popular.
3. My uncle, _____ (he is an engineer), has never been to Ireland.
4. The party, _____ (it was to celebrate my aunt's birthday), finished quite early.
5. Paul is the student _____ (it's his birthday today).
6. That's the house _____ (they're having the party there).

4 ●●● Join the sentences. Use the relative pronouns in bold.

1. That's the man. He took our photo. **WHO**
   That's the man who took our photo.
2. The party was great. It was at my friend's house. **WHICH**
   _____
3. The leaving party went on for a long time. We ate lots of nice food there. **WHERE**
   _____
4. My uncle is coming to our dinner party. He's a doctor. **WHO**
   _____
5. A house-warming party is a celebration. You have it when you move into a new home. **WHICH**
   _____
6. Sheila is the girl. Her mother bought her a concert ticket for her birthday. **WHOSE**
   _____
7. This is the place. We had our prom there. **WHERE**
   _____
8. Tom is my cousin. His team won the school championship. **WHOSE**
   _____

I can be specific about people, things and places.

On the Portal
Extra Practice Activities: Lesson 9.2

9.3 Reading and Vocabulary
Special days

1 Complete the sentences with prepositions.
1. My little brother is crazy *about* superheroes. I think he wants to be one!
2. I'm very fond _____ Mexican food. I love spicy dishes.
3. We're big fans _____ football in my family. We always go to games when we can.
4. Luca has a real passion _____ photography.
5. I don't think you're really _____ old films, are you? You seem bored.
6. I used to be keen _____ swimming, but I'm not any more.

2 Read the article quickly and match paragraphs A–D with headings 1–4.
1. Book Lovers' Day
2. Handwriting Day
3. Compliment Day
4. Watermelon Day

3 Which of the ideas in the article in Exercise 2 are suitable for the people below? Match each person to one of the special days (A–D). There is one extra day.

Christophe ☐
I'm really into games. I spend all my time playing them online and because of this, I don't eat very well. I usually just grab something quickly so I can carry on playing. I'd like to eat more healthily, but I don't really know much about food or how to cook.

Sara ☐
I recently had to write an essay in an exam, and it really hurt my hand. That's when I realised I never really do this anymore. I seem to spend all my time in front of a computer screen, reading online articles and social media posts. I really should get in touch with my gran too. I haven't spoken to her for ages now.

Shaun ☐
My family recently moved to this area and I don't really have many friends here. I'd like to talk to people at school more, but I'm not very keen on speaking to people I don't know very well. I just don't really know how to start a conversation.

Four special days which celebrate things worth doing every day anyway

A Celebrate this day by writing a letter – that's right, a letter – to a friend or someone in your family. You might not be keen on old-fashioned writing, but think about how they'll feel when they receive something that you've gone to so much effort to make. Turn off your computer, phone, laptop or tablet, and then pick up a pen and paper to send some joy to a special person.

_____

B This fruit is (rightly) sometimes described as a 'superfood'. It's ninety-two percent water and contains vitamins A, C and antioxidants. You can go all in and celebrate this day by having watermelon for every meal or just take the time to discover how including different fresh fruit and vegetables in your diet can give both your physical and mental health a boost.

_____

C A day all about reading books. What's not to love? On this day, make some time to sit down in a comfortable chair and read a book. Reading isn't just entertaining. It's good for your health: it reduces stress and it can help you sleep better. You could even throw a book party: dress up as your favourite characters and have some fun!

_____

D On this day, take time to say nice things to people around you. Think of something you like and respect about a family member or friend and tell them it. You'll discover that it doesn't just make them happy, it makes you happy too. Once you start doing this, you may want to keep complimenting people every day!

_____

I can understand an article about special days.

9.4 Grammar
Direct and indirect questions

GRAMMAR Direct and indirect questions

	Direct	Indirect
Wh- questions	Which terminal are we leaving from?	Can/Could you remind me which terminal we're leaving from?
	How long will the flight be?	I'd like to know how long the flight will be.
Wh- questions with do/does/did	What does it mean?	Do you know what it means?
	Why did you keep it a secret?	I wonder why you kept it a secret.
Yes/No questions	Is there a pool in the hotel?	Have you any idea if there is a pool in the hotel?
	Can I film you?	Do you mind if I film you?

1 ● Match 1–6 with a–f to make questions. Then decide if they are direct (D) or indirect (I) questions.

1 c D What time
2 ☐ ☐ Could you tell me where
3 ☐ ☐ Where
4 ☐ ☐ I was wondering what
5 ☐ ☐ Does Margaret
6 ☐ ☐ Do you have any idea if Katie

a   is the station?
b   speaks Italian?
c   ~~do you get up in the morning?~~
d   like French food?
e   your friend is from?
f   you want for your birthday.

2 ● Choose the correct option.
1 Could you tell me what time *the film starts* / *does the film start*?
2 Do you know where *is the parade* / *the parade is*?
3 I was wondering *is Stanley* / *if Stanley is* keen on having a party for his birthday.
4 Do you have any idea when *Amber turns* / *turns Amber* twenty-one?
5 Do you know *where is there* / *if there is* a bank near here?
6 Could you tell me *do* / *if* you like broccoli?

3 ●● Order the words in brackets to complete the indirect questions.
1 Could you tell me *where the bathroom is* (bathroom / the / where / is)?
2 Do you know _____ (it's / if / expensive)?
3 I was wondering _____ (leaves / the bus / time / what).
4 Do you have any idea _____ (arrived / the parcel / if / has)?
5 Could you tell me _____ (old / you / how / are)?

4 ●● Complete the indirect questions.
1 Where's the party?
   Do you know *where the party is*?
2 What are you doing for your birthday?
   I was wondering _____.
3 Does James have a sister?
   Could you tell me _____?
4 How much are the tickets?
   Do you have any idea _____?
5 Where did you go to school?
   I was wondering _____.

5 ●●● Use the direct questions below to complete the indirect questions in the dialogue. There is one extra question.

| Are you enjoying it? ~~Could I ask you a few questions?~~ |
| Is this your first visit to the festival? |
| What are you going to do after it finishes? |
| Where do you live? |

A: Excuse me. I'm doing a survey about festivals. I was wondering ¹*if I could ask you a few questions*.
B: Yes, of course.
A: Thank you. Firstly, could you tell me ²_____?
B: Yes, it is.
A: I'd like to know ³_____.
B: Yes, I'm having a fantastic time!
A: Thank you. And do you have any idea ⁴_____?
B: Oh, I'm just going to go home.
A: That's all. Thank you very much.
B: You're welcome.

Unit 9 | 94 | I can ask questions politely.

9.5 Listening and Vocabulary

Happy birthday to you!

1 Complete the dialogues with the correct form of the verbs below.

> feel   look   ~~smell~~   sound   taste

1. A: Are these eggs OK to eat?
   B: Ugh no, they _smell_ terrible! Throw them away!
2. A: What's your favourite fruit?
   B: Watermelon. It just _____ delicious.
3. A: How did your performance go?
   B: Well, I _____ terrified at the start, but then it went really well at the end.
4. A: I think there's something wrong with my computer.
   B: Yes, it _____ noisy when you start it up. That's not right, is it?
5. A: Do you like my new hair style?
   B: Yes, you _____ incredible!

2 🔊 9.1 Listen to a radio interview. Which birthday tradition are the people discussing?
   a singing along to famous songs
   b eating birthday cake
   c singing a song

3 🔊 9.1 Listen again and choose the correct answer.
1. According to Scott Hurley, the song is one of the
   a oldest songs in the world.
   b most translated songs in the world.
   c most recognised songs in the world.
2. Patty and Mildred Hill
   a composed the song for the piano.
   b first printed the song.
   c first recorded the song.
3. What happens after people sing the song in Canada?
   a They sing an extension to the song.
   b They give presents to the person whose birthday it is.
   c They eat special food.
4. In Brazil, an extra part of the song refers to
   a the Portuguese language.
   b a children's character.
   c the parents of the person whose birthday it is.
5. The Mars rover *Curiosity* sang the song to
   a a planet.   b a president.   c itself.

I can understand a radio interview about the history of a song.

On the Portal
Extra Practice Activities: Lesson 9.5

9.6 Speaking
Being polite

1 🔊 **9.2** Listen and repeat the phrases.

SPEAKING — **Being polite**

Attracting attention
Excuse me, can I just get past?
Sorry (to bother you), but can I open the window?

Making and responding to polite requests
A: I was wondering if you could help me.
A: Do you mind if I sit here?
B: No, go ahead./Sorry, but this seat is taken.
A: Would you mind passing the salt?
B: Of course not.
A: Could you pass me the salt, please?
B: Yes, of course. Here you are.
A: Do you happen to know if there's a bank near here?
B: I'm sorry, I don't know.
A: I wonder if you could do something for me.
B: Sure./Sorry, I can't.

Giving and responding to thanks
A: That's really kind of you.   B: It's quite all right.
A: I really appreciate it.   B: It's no problem.
A: Thanks (so/very much).   B: You're welcome.

2 Complete the sentences with the words below. There is one extra word.

> appreciate   bother   ~~excuse~~   happen   kind
> mind   pass   thank   wonder

1 *Excuse* me, do you know what the time is?
2 Could you _____ me the newspaper, please?
3 Do you _____ to know if the food is good here?
4 I _____ if you could do something for me.
5 Sorry to _____ you, but can you give me a hand?
6 Thanks, I really _____ it.
7 _____ you so much. I couldn't have done this without your help.
8 Would you _____ helping me lift this?

3 Choose the correct option.
1 *Thank* / *Thanks* you very much.
2 I was *wonder* / *wondering* if you could help me.
3 Could you *turning* / *turn* the light on?
4 Would you mind *sit* / *sitting* over there?
5 Yes, of course. *Here* / *That* you are.
6 Thanks, I really appreciate *you* / *it*.

4 Complete the sentences with one word in each gap.
1 I wonder *if* you could help me.
2 'Could I borrow your pen?' 'Yes, of course. _____ you are.'
3 That's really kind _____ you.
4 'Do you mind _____ I read your newspaper?' 'No, _____ ahead.'
5 'Thanks for all your help.' 'It's _____ all right.'
6 Do you _____ to know if there's a post office near here?
7 The flowers were beautiful! Thank you so _____.

5 🔊 **9.3** Choose the correct option to complete the dialogue. Then listen and check.

Driver: Excuse ¹*you* / *me* / *it*, are you Ian?
Ian: That's right. Do you ²*mind* / *wonder* / *want* if I sit here in the front?
Driver: ³*Course* / *Yes* / *No*, go ahead.
Ian: I ⁴*wonder* / *mind* / *would* if I could ask you where you're from.
Driver: Sure, I'm from Poland.
Ian: Really? My friend is Polish too. His name's Jan. Where in Poland are you from?
Driver: I'm from Toruń.
Ian: Ah, my friend is from Katowice. Do you ⁵*happen* / *quite* / *wonder* to know if there's a Polish food shop around here?
Driver: I'm ⁶*all right* / *sure* / *sorry*, I don't know. But I know there's an online shop that does deliveries. I'll give you their number when we get to your destination if you like.
Ian: That's really kind ⁷*for* / *of* / *from* you, thank you.
Driver: You're ⁸*thanks* / *ahead* / *welcome*!

Unit 9 — 96 — I can use polite phrases in conversation.

On the Portal
Extra Practice Activities: Lesson 9.6

9.7 Writing
An informal invitation

1 Read the email quickly. What does Kate want Mia to do?
a   help him organise a holiday
b   come to a party
c   go on holiday with him and his friends

Hi Mia,

How are ¹*things*?

I'm writing to let you know that we're having a weekend away camping in July to celebrate the end of the school year and kick off the summer holidays in style! I know we go to different schools, but would you ² _____ to come? At the moment it's just Jo, my dad and me, but we hope to get lots more people to come and celebrate. We'll have games and music, and we've got lots of camping equipment, so you don't need to bring any.

I'd really like to ³ _____ you the New Forest. We're ⁴ _____ to stay on a great little campsite with a swimming pool, and near a lake, so you could do with bringing some swimming trunks.

I ⁵ _____ you can make it and celebrate with us. It would be great to see you again and I can't wait to hear your news!

⁶ _____ soon,

Kate

---

2 Complete the email with the words below.

hope   like   planning   show   speak   ~~things~~

3 Put the parts of the email a–e in order. Then match phrases 1–7 with parts a–e.

a ☐ explaining your plans in more detail
b ☐ *1* starting your email
c ☐ ending your email
d ☐ offering an invitation
e ☐ before you finish

1 ☐ How are your summer holidays going?
2 ☐ See you soon.
3 ☐ Do you want to meet up?
4 ☐ I'm really looking forward to seeing you.
5 ☐ Let me know as soon as possible.
6 ☐ Do you fancy coming to … ?
7 ☐ What have you been up to?

4 Complete the notes about Stefania's party with the words below.

display   festival   house   last weekend
~~to email~~   visit

- remember ¹*to email* Liz to invite her to my birthday party
- where: my ² _____
- when: ³ _____ in August
- things to do/show her: ⁴ _____ the shopping centre in town; local ⁵ _____ with firework ⁶ _____

WRITING TIME

5 Write Stefania's email to Liz.

1 Find ideas
Include this information:
- ask her how she is.
- invite her to your birthday party.
- give details about the party, saying what you want to do and what you want to show her.

2 Plan and write
- Organise your ideas into paragraphs. Use Chris's email in Exercise 1 to help you.
- Write a draft of your email.

3 Check
- Check language: have you used informal language?
- Check grammar: have you used relative clauses correctly?
- Write the final version of your email.

I can write an email inviting a friend to a celebration.

My Language File

WORDLIST 🔊 9.4

Celebrations
ceremony (n) _____
costume (n) _____
custom (n) _____
festival (n) _____
firework display (n) _____
parade (n) _____
special occasion (n) _____
tradition (n) _____

Word friends
(special occasions)
blow out candles _____
bring bad luck _____
bring good luck _____
celebrate a birthday _____
follow the tradition of _____
get together with _____
light candles _____
light fireworks _____
organise a party _____
prepare a meal _____
put up decorations _____
stay up late _____
throw a party _____
turn a year older _____
turn eighteen _____
unwrap presents _____
wrap presents _____

Types of celebrations
carnival (n) _____
family get-together (n) _____
fancy-dress party (n) _____
formal dinner (n) _____
school prom (n) _____
street party (n) _____
surprise party (n) _____
wedding reception (n) _____

Phrases to express likes
be a big fan of _____
be crazy about _____
be fond of _____
be into/get into _____
be keen on _____
have a passion for _____

Sense verbs
feel terrified _____
look incredible _____
smell terrible _____
sound noisy _____
taste delicious _____

Extra words
attend (v) _____
attraction (n) _____
barbecue (n) _____
brightly coloured (adj) _____

calendar (n) _____
close friend (n) _____
count down to (v) _____
dress up (v) _____
entertain (v) _____
event (n) _____
hang out (v) _____
Independence Day (n) _____
live concert/music (n) _____
masquerade ball (n) _____
meet up (v) _____
midnight (n) _____
New Year's Eve (n) _____
outdoor activity (n) _____
party (v) _____
powder (n) _____
ring a bell _____
rotten (n) _____
rub (v) _____
show (n) _____
stay overnight _____
take part _____
take place _____
Thanksgiving (n) _____
traditional (adj) _____

Sounds good!
Go ahead. _____
You'll never guess … ! _____

MY LANGUAGE NOTES

My favourite words/expressions from this unit

Self-check

Vocabulary

1 Choose the correct option.
1. Would you like to go to the school *tradition / prom* with me?
2. When my sister got married, she had a really nice *tradition / ceremony* on the beach.
3. Diwali is a *festival / reception* which takes place around the world in October or November.
4. Last weekend, we had a lovely family *get-together / come-together* and I saw all my relatives.
5. For my eighteenth birthday, my friends and family *threw / made* a big party for me.
6. For my mum's birthday, I *wrapped / prepared* a nice meal for her.
7. I'd like to have a formal *fancy dress / dinner* on my birthday, but most of my friends would think it's boring.
8. Can you help me *hold / put* up these decorations?
9. When did your brother *get / turn* eighteen?
10. You look tired. Did you *wake / stay* up late last night?

2 Complete the words in the sentences.
1. You look smart! Is it a s_____ occasion?
2. My cousin had her wedding r_____ in a football stadium!
3. What c_____ are you going to wear to the fancy-dress party?
4. Every year, Rio de Janeiro is home to the world's biggest c_____.
5. We're going to throw a s_____ party for Helen on her birthday. Don't say anything to her!
6. Would you like to u_____ your presents now or after breakfast?
7. How do you usually c_____ your birthday?
8. On my birthday I usually get t_____ with a few friends and have a meal.
9. Let's l_____ some fireworks in the garden tonight!
10. During the festival, we took part in a p_____ along the streets.

Grammar

3 Complete the sentences with *which*, *who*, *where* or *whose*.
1. That's the girl _____ birthday party it is.
2. The festival, _____ is held every year, attracts people from all over the world.
3. The spectators, _____ were wearing traditional costumes, clapped and cheered.
4. That's the place _____ we went for our holiday last year.
5. In Canada, _____ they sing a different version of the song, people usually make a special cake.
6. That's the man _____ daughter won the competition.
7. Is that the girl _____ you met at the party?
8. That's the boy _____ mum is a journalist.

4 Complete the indirect questions.
1. What time does the parade start?
   Could you tell me _____?
2. Where can I catch a bus?
   I was wondering _____.
3. Did Mark go to the party?
   Do you know _____?
4. How old are you?
   Can you tell me _____?
5. Have they sold many tickets?
   Do you know _____?
6. Where will the concert be?
   Could you remind me _____?
7. What does it mean?
   Do you know _____?

Speaking

5 Complete the dialogue with one word in each gap.

Ava: ¹_____ to bother you. Do you ²_____ if I sit here?
Sue: No, go ³_____.
Ava: Could you ⁴_____ the tomato sauce, please?
Sue: Yes, of course. ⁵_____ you are.
Ava: Thanks.

YOUR SCORE

Vocabulary: __/20   Speaking: __/5
Grammar: __/15   Total: __/40

Reading Time 3

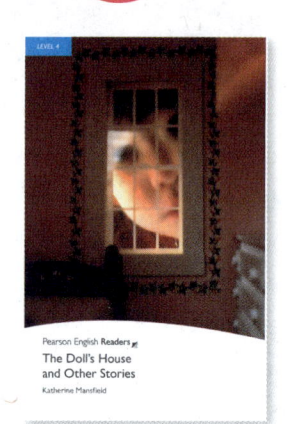

The Garden Party

It was a perfect day for a garden party. The gardener had been working since early in the morning, cutting the grass. The roses looked perfect.

During breakfast, the men came to put up the marquee.

'Where do you want them to put the marquee, mother?'

'My dear child, don't ask me. This year, you children must do everything. You'll have to go, Laura.'

Laura went out into the garden, still holding a piece of bread and butter. She loved having to arrange things. But when she saw the men standing there with all their equipment, she felt shy. She wished she was not holding the bread and butter.

'Good morning,' she said, copying her mother's voice. But that sounded wrong and she continued, like a little girl, 'Oh – er – have you come – is it about the marquee?'

'That's right.'

The men were friendly, and Laura felt better. She wanted to say 'What a beautiful morning!' but she must be business-like.

'What about there?' she pointed.

But the men did not agree with her.

'Look here, miss, that's the place. Against those trees. Over there.'

She did not want the marquee to hide the beautiful trees, but the men were already moving off towards the trees. But the men were so nice. She liked them better than the boys she danced with and the boys who came to supper on Sunday night. She took a big bite of bread and butter.

Then someone called from the house, 'Laura, where are you? Telephone, Laura!'

'Coming!' She ran back to the house, across the garden. In the hall, her father and brother were getting ready to go to the office.

'I say, Laura,' said her brother, Laurie, speaking very fast, 'could you just look at my coat before this afternoon?'

'I will,' she said. Suddenly, she added, 'Oh, I do love parties, don't you?'

'Yes,' he said in his warm and boyish voice, 'but don't forget the telephone.'

All the doors in the house were open. People ran from room to room, calling to each other. There was a strange sound – they were moving the piano. The front doorbell rang. It was the man from the flower shop. But there were so many beautiful flowers – Laura could not believe it.

'There must be some mistake!'

Her mother suddenly appeared. 'It's quite right. I ordered them. Aren't they lovely!'

They tried out the piano. Laura's sister sang. Then a servant came in and asked about the sandwiches. There were fifteen different kinds of sandwiches. Then a man came to deliver some cream cakes from the baker's shop.

'Bring them in and put them on the table,' ordered the cook.

Laura and her sister tried some of the cream cakes. Then Laura suggested, 'Let's go into the garden, out by the back way.'

But they could not get through the back door. The cook and Sadie were there talking to the baker's man.

Something had happened.

Their faces were worried. The baker's man was telling them something.

'What's the matter? What's happened?'

'There's been a horrible accident,' said the cook. 'A man killed.'

'Killed! Where? How? When?'

Before you read

1 Match sentences 1–4 with pictures A–D.
1 We put up a marquee for the party in case it rained.
2 We had some friends come over for supper.
3 Push the doorbell so they know we're here.
4 My mum made some lovely cream cakes for my party.

2 Look at the title of the story and the picture. Choose the correct option.
1 The weather is *excellent / not suitable* for a garden party.
2 The men have come to *work / have fun*.
3 The people seem *cheerful / upset*.
4 The girl *shows the men / doesn't know* how to arrange things for the party.

While you read

3 🔊 RT3.1 Read and listen to the story. Put events a–g in the order they happen.
a ☐ Someone calls Laura from the house.
b ☐ The cream cakes arrive.
c ☐ They receive some terrible news.
d ☐ The gardener cuts the grass.
e ☐ Laura's father and brother go to work.
f ☐ The marquee arrives.
g ☐ The flowers arrive.

After you read

4 Complete the sentences with the correct form of the verbs below.

| agree   come   move   put   try |

1 Can you help me _____ up the marquee before the party?
2 I was about to tell her it was OK, but she was already _____ off towards the house.
3 If you have a party with music, do you _____ out the playlist with your friends before?
4 How often do you have friends _____ to dinner at your house?
5 I _____ with my friends when they told me I should have a big party for my eighteenth birthday!

5 What happens next? Answer the questions. Then read the summary below and check your answers.
1 How do you think the man died?
2 Does the party still happen?
3 What do you think happens in the rest of the story?

> Laura and her mother find out that the young man fell off his horse, hit his head and died. Laura thinks they should cancel the party, but nobody agrees with her. After the party, Laura's mother decides to send a basket of food to the family of the man who lost his life, and asks Laura to take it. Laura feels strange about it and doesn't want to at first, but she takes the basket to the neighbours anyway. When she arrives, she meets the man's wife, who is upset and crying. The wife's sister comes in and talks to Laura, and Laura feels better.

6 **WRAP UP** Complete the information about the story.

Title: _____
Type: *love story / short story / crime story*
Main characters: _____
_____
Important object: _____
My opinion: ☆☆☆☆☆

Exam Time 1 — Listening — Units 1–3

1 🔊 **ET1–3.1** Listen and choose the correct answer.

> **Exam tip**
> Choose the answers that you think are correct the first time you listen, then check your answers on the second listening.

1 What is the boy concerned about in his city?
  A ☐   B ☐   C ☐

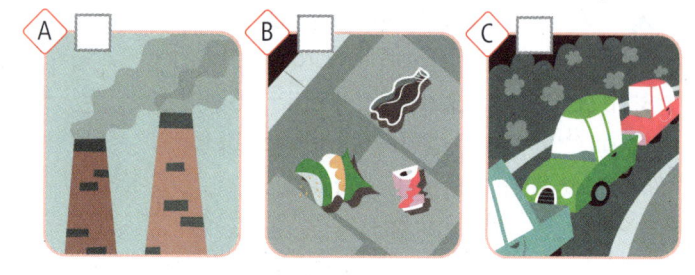

2 What can you recycle at the school?
  A ☐   B ☐   C ☐

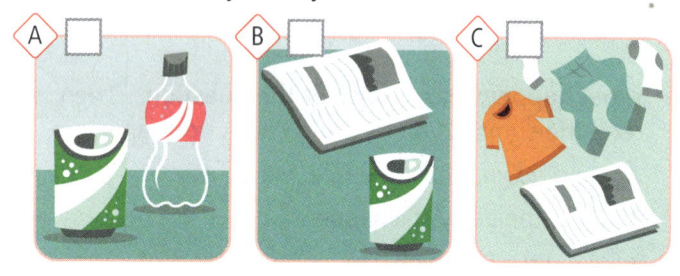

3 Which place are the people going to clean?
  A ☐   B ☐   C ☐

4 What has the boy just bought?
  A ☐   B ☐   C ☐

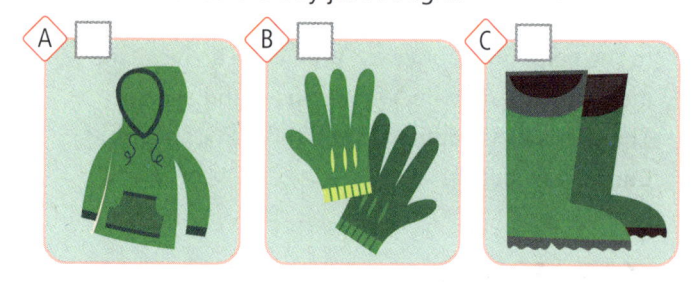

5 Which boots does the girl buy?
  A ☐   B ☐   C ☐

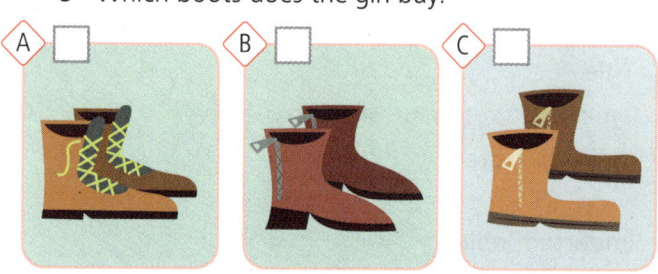

2 🔊 **ET1–3.2** Listen to an interview with Jake, a young fashion designer. Choose the correct answer.

> **Exam tip**
> The questions come in the same order as the information in the recording. If you miss the answer to a question, leave it and move on to the next question, then try to answer it the second time you listen.

1 What is Jake planning to do in the summer holidays?
  a relax and have a rest
  b prepare for a fashion show
  c go on holiday with his parents

2 Who first suggested that he should design clothes?
  a his sister
  b his aunt
  c his parents

3 According to Jake, what is the most important quality you need to be successful?
  a You need to be very creative.
  b You need to be organised and reliable.
  c You need to be determined.

4 What makes Jake's clothes so popular?
  a You make them yourself in the shop.
  b Customers can choose exactly what the clothes look like.
  c They are cheaper than clothes in High Street shops.

5 What does Jake intend to do when he leaves school?
  a work full-time on his own business
  b go to college to study Fashion Design
  c get some work experience with a fashion designer

6 What would Jake most like to do?
  a inspire other young people to become successful
  b earn lots of money
  c become a famous fashion designer

3 🔊 **ET1–3.3** Listen. Then listen again and write down what you hear during each pause.

102 Exam Time 1

Exam Time 1 — Reading and Writing — Units 1–3

4 These people all want to try a new experience in the city where they live. On the right are descriptions of eight things to do. Read the texts and decide which experience (A–H) would be the most suitable for each person (1–5).

> **Exam tip**
> Read the descriptions of the people first. Then read the texts and underline any information which matches the information in the descriptions. Finally, match the people with the texts.

1 Charlotte likes cooking and finds it relaxing, but is looking for a new challenge. She already knows how to make lots of different types of food, but would like to learn how to make different types of drinks.

2 Steve has lived in the same city all his life and always goes to the same places, so he's quite bored of it. He would like to travel and discover new places, but he doesn't have free time to do it.

3 Lee is interested in learning more about how to protect the environment. She feels disappointed when she sees how much rubbish there is in the countryside. She especially loves animals and loves learning all about them.

4 Carla is really keen on fashion. She's been feeling bored with her appearance lately and would like to try something completely different. She doesn't really like big events and would like to spend some time experimenting with her appearance.

5 Amir feels annoyed when he sees how dirty the city is. He doesn't have many friends and would like to meet new people with similar interests. He's also interested in protecting the environment.

New experiences to try in the city

A Free fashion festival
This weekend, St Helen's Park is filled with clothes, models and high fashion. Come along in the afternoon to see all the exciting, fashionable clothes we have to show. There will also be celebrity appearances from top designers and models, who will be signing copies of their books and speaking to members of the public.

B Become a barista!
Do you like good coffee? Would you like to become king or queen of the coffee shop? Why not come along and learn how to make your own with this afternoon course. From sweet, spicy Mexican coffee to Indian coffee and healthy fruit drinks – learn how to make them all and impress your friends!

C Organise a local clean-up
Are you disappointed with all the litter in our city? Then get your friends together and organise a local clean-up group. Or let us introduce you to your new group – who could soon be your new friends! We can send you bags and gloves, as well as information on how to recycle the things you find.

D Hidden city
If you're looking to have an adventure this summer, we offer tours to all those little places you never knew existed in the city. Hidden parks, specialist shops and quiet cafés are just a few of the places we'll help you to discover. We know where they all are – and so should you!

E Makeover time
Come and have a makeover! If you've been feeling worn-out and scruffy recently, then come and spend a few hours with us. Our stylists can give you advice on what clothes to wear. We can even paint your nails or dye your hair. So what are you waiting for? Come and give it a go!

F Rescue centre
Visit Tynedale Animal Shelter and find out about what we do. We have over fifty different species of endangered animals that we've rescued from danger. Come and make friends with them today and discover how you can help protect them. This is a really fun day out and a truly enjoyable experience.

G Facing your fears
Are you afraid of heights? Visit our phobia centre, where we work with you to boost your confidence. We can also help with a fear of flying. At the end of the day with us, you get to climb our tower and we promise you'll get a buzz out of it!

H Cooking course
Does the thought of cooking make you feel stressed? If so, then our four-hour intensive cooking course is just for you. We show you how to make a range of delicious dishes from around the world and also give tips on what healthy drinks go well with them. Challenge yourself to become a top chef!

Exam Time 1 — Reading and Writing   Units 1–3

5 Read the texts and choose the correct answer.

Exam tip: Look at the words before and after the gap to help you choose the correct answer.

1
♻ This ____ bin is for glass, plastic and paper only.
PLEASE DO NOT PUT OTHER LITTER INTO IT.

a pollution   b recycling   c renewable

2
James,
I've just been to the new climbing wall in town. It was great – I ____ to get to the top! Do you want to give it a go with me next weekend?
Matt

a managed   b reached   c succeeded

3
End of summer sale
20% ____ on all sandals!
That's right – they were £10, now only £8!

a bargain   b price   c discount

4
Join our project. Help us ____ the beach on 7 October. If you're interested, sign your name below. It'll be messy work, so wear some old clothes!

a reduce   b throw away   c clean up

5
Sarah,
Julia phoned and asked you to meet her at the shopping centre at 3 p.m. I've left you some money on the kitchen table. Please get yourself a ____ top to wear to your cousin's wedding.
See you later,
Mum x

a gold   b smart   c scruffy

6 You have recently moved to Australia with your family. Read the email from your English-speaking friend Tim and the notes you have made. Tick the four things that you need to include in your reply. Then write your reply to Tim in about 100 words.

Exam tip: Make sure you include all the information from your notes. Write what the notes say – do not use your own ideas.

✉
Hi!
How was the move to Australia? Was it easy or difficult? We all miss you already! I spend quite a lot of time with Jamie and the others at the weekend. Tell me about your new life there. I bet the weather is great! Have you made any friends yet? What have you found difficult about your new life there? Let me know how you're getting on.
Bye for now,
Tim

Notes:
- Me too!
- We all miss you already!
- Yes – tell him about a new friend
- Yes! It's …
- I've found … because …

a ☐ something about the weather in Australia
b ☐ ask about Jamie and the others
c ☐ a description of someone you've met
d ☐ say you miss your friends
e ☐ something you've found easy and the reason why
f ☐ something you've found difficult and the reason why

Exam Time 2 — Listening — Units 1–6

1 🔊 **ET1–6.1** Listen and choose the correct answer.

1 What would the girl like to do?
   a go hang-gliding   b do a space walk
   c walk on the moon
2 What time is the boy's interview?
   a 1.30 p.m.   b 2.30 p.m.
   c 3.30 p.m.
3 How much will the girl be earning this summer?
   a £10.50 per hour   b £11.50 per hour
   c £12.00 per hour
4 What should the boy do?
   a go to school   b stay in bed
   c take some pills
5 What is the girl suffering from now?
   a an allergy   b a headache
   c the flu

2 🔊 **ET1–6.2** Listen to some information about a new museum. Complete the notes with the missing information.

> **Exam tip**
> Read the notes before you listen and think about what type of word or phrase you need for each gap (e.g. a name, a number, a place).

Space Museum

Date of opening: [1] *23 February*
Number of exhibition rooms: [2] _____
Ticket price for under 16s: [3] £ _____
Price includes entry to the [4] _____
Full-size model of part of the [5] _____
Visit the website at: [6] _____

3 🔊 **ET1–6.3** Listen to an interview with Kizzie, who has just got onto an astronaut training programme. Choose the correct answer.

> **Exam tip**
> Read each question very carefully. All the answers might seem correct, but only one will match the recording exactly.

1 How is Kizzie feeling about starting her training?
   a impatient and ready to start
   b nervous about everything she will have to learn
   c excited that she will meet the others on the programme
2 Kizzie first became interested in space
   a at school.
   b through a friend at university.
   c after watching a TV programme.
3 The training to become an astronaut
   a involves only practice and no theory.
   b lasts for over two years.
   c involves a short trip to the International Space Station.
4 When do most astronauts have health problems?
   a during take-off and landing
   b after about three months in space
   c when they return home after their trip
5 What is Kizzie not looking forward to about going to the space station?
   a eating horrible food
   b missing members of her family
   c working very hard on experiments
6 What would Kizzie like to do one day?
   a travel to Mars
   b encourage other young people to become interested in space
   c make discoveries that could help people

4 🔊 **ET1–6.4** Listen. Then listen again and write down what you hear during each pause.

Exam Time 2 — Reading and Writing — Units 1–6

5 Read the blog post and choose the correct answer.

1. What is the writer trying to do in this text?
   a advise people not to work with Aid First
   b describe her experience in Sierra Leone
   c show readers how good things are in Sierra Leone
   d say why you should work for Aid First

2. What made her decide to apply for the job?
   a a phone call from Aid First
   b something she saw on TV
   c something she read
   d a colleague's advice

3. What does she say about children under five who have malaria?
   a they need urgent medical attention
   b they usually die
   c they can't survive the journey to hospital
   d she wanted to send them all to hospital

4. What does she say about the experience at the end of the article?
   a she doesn't want to do it again
   b she was afraid of getting ill
   c it was difficult to please the people she worked with
   d it was hard, but she is pleased she did it

My year in Sierra Leone

Two years ago I was working as a doctor at a hospital in London, when a colleague said to me, 'If you had the chance to change something in the world, what would you do?' At that time I told him that I hadn't thought about it before, so I didn't really know. But later that night I saw an advertisement in a magazine for Aid First, a charity which sends doctors and medical staff to countries where there are emergency situations. I decided to call them and tell them that I wanted to help.

It took me six months to apply for the job because you have to do a lot of tests and paperwork. Finally, they told me I could go, and ready sent me to Sierra Leone, where one of the biggest problems was malaria. I worked in a small team of three and it was very hard work. If I'd known how hard it was, I would have prepared myself more carefully, I think.

We worked very long hours, often into the night, and although we had one day off per week, we often had to help out then too.

The hardest time was in the rainy season. The number of small children with malaria during this time almost doubled, but we didn't have any extra staff or facilities. If a child under five gets malaria, they need to see a doctor quickly or they might die. Sometimes we had to make difficult decisions about whether to send sick children to the hospital or keep them with us. It was a long journey to the hospital and if they were too ill, they wouldn't survive.

Although it wasn't easy, I'm pleased I did it and I would do it again if I had the chance. It's difficult to see so many people so badly affected by diseases, but the small victories you have when you see people get better make it all worth it.

Exam Time 2 — Reading and Writing — Units 1–6

6 Complete the advert with sentences a–h. There are three extra sentences that you do not need.

a This year, the job fair is on a Saturday, not on a working day.
b It's difficult to find a job, but we can help you.
c We also have over twenty years' experience of organising job fairs.
d Visit our website to read some of their reviews.
e These are the types of questions you need to ask at an interview.
f This is so that we have enough time to create your online 'space'.
g But it's not just unemployed people we work with.
h First, write a CV and upload it to our website.

7 Read the leaflet and answer the questions.

Emplotech Online Job Fair

Emplotech will be offering its third annual online job fair on Saturday 15 March. We are the biggest recruitment company in the country. ^{1}____ Whether you are a company looking for the right person or someone looking for a job, our job fair is most definitely the place to be.

If you want to attend, you will need to register at least two weeks in advance. ^{2}____ All you need to do is provide us with the information we need and we will create an attractive page for you on our website.

We offer the following:

For companies
We are the country's biggest provider of recruitment services. If you register with us, we will give you access to thousands of people looking for a job. ^{3}____ We also work with highly skilled staff looking to change their careers. Many companies have already benefited from our experience in matching the right people with the right position. We have hundreds of satisfied customers! ^{4}____

For candidates
We offer access to hundreds of companies looking for staff. If you want to find a new job, we will help you through the process. It is very easy and will not take you more than half an hour. ^{5}____ Then look at the jobs on offer and choose the ones that you want to apply for. If the company likes your CV, they will contact you and arrange an interview. Even if you are not successful, you will gain experience of applying and having an interview. So what have you got to lose?

To register for this year's Emplotech Online Job Fair, click here.

1 Who will meet you when you get to the hospital? _a nurse_
2 When must you wear your wristband?
   _____
3 What do you need to tell the hospital about?
   _____
4 Who will decide when you leave hospital?
   _____
5 What will your doctor explain how to take?
   _____

Your stay in hospital

On arrival
A nurse will greet you and check your personal and medical details. We will also give you a wristband with your name on it. Please wear this at all times.

We also ask you to:
- tell us about any allergies you have.
- give us any medicines you have brought with you.
- put all your valuables in the locker next to your bed.

Leaving hospital
- You can usually leave by 11 a.m. Sometimes this might not be possible, however. Your doctor will discuss this with you on the day.
- We will give you back any medicines you brought with you. Your doctor will explain how to take any new medicines.
- Please arrange for someone to collect you on the day you leave.

Exam tip
Before you start writing, plan what to include in your answer and make notes. You can then focus on using a range of grammar and vocabulary while you write.

8 You have just finished doing a summer job. Write a blog post describing your experience. Write 70–90 words and include the following information.
- the reason why you did the job
- how you felt when you started it
- what you've learned from the job

Exam Time 3 — Listening — Units 1–9

1 🔊 **ET1–9.1** Listen and choose the correct answer.

> **Exam tip**
> Think about the differences between the three pictures for each item. This will help you to listen for the right information.

1 How did the girl learn about the new perfume?
   A ☐   B ☐   C ☐

2 What time will the art gallery close today?
   A ☐   B ☐   C ☐

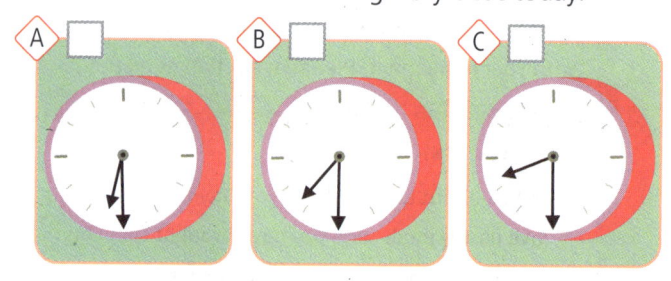

3 What does the boy always look at first on the news website?
   A ☐   B ☐   C ☐

4 What is the date of the school prom?
   A ☐ JUNE 21   B ☐ JUNE 23   C ☐ JUNE 25

5 What event is the girl looking forward to?
   A ☐   B ☐   C ☐

2 🔊 **ET1–9.2** Listen to some information about a parade. Complete the notes with the missing information.

> **Summer parade**
> Place to meet: [1] *the park*
> Time parade starts: [2] _____
> Remember to bring [3] _____
> Mr Kean will bring [4] _____
> Mrs Denton will help with [5] _____
> Day ends with a [6] _____

3 🔊 **ET1–9.3** Listen to a conversation about animal communication and choose the correct answer.

1 Jack thinks that birds
   a don't sing to each other.
   b don't really have a language.
   c warn other birds about possible dangers.

2 How does Jack feel when Tess tells him how far whale sounds can travel?
   a surprised
   b uninterested
   c annoyed

3 Jack knows that dogs can communicate with humans because
   a they can understand human words.
   b he read about it.
   c he has experienced it.

4 Dogs can also communicate with other animals
   a with sounds.
   b with the way they walk.
   c with body language.

5 Chimpanzees show other chimpanzees they like them by
   a touching them.
   b waving their arms at them.
   c making sounds.

6 What does Tess suggest Jack does?
   a learn more about chimpanzees
   b borrow her book
   c find out more information on the internet

4 🔊 **ET1-9.4** Listen. Then listen again and write down what you hear during each pause.

108 Exam Time 3

Exam Time 3 — Reading and Writing — Units 1–9

5 Complete the blog post with sentences a–h. There are three extra sentences.

Exam tip: You do not have to start with the first gap. You can complete the easier ones first.

My carnival experience

I'm a member of a dance group, and earlier this year, I won a prize to go to Rio de Janeiro in Brazil and take part in what many people believe is the largest festival on Earth – the Rio carnival. The carnival has been running since 1723 and it gets bigger each year. ¹_____

I arrived a few days before, after a twelve-hour flight from London, so I was very tired. The director of the samba school met me and drove me to the fashionable district of Ipanema, where I was staying in a hostel. ²_____

Carnival officially starts on the Friday and goes on all the next week. ³_____ On Saturday and Sunday nights, the samba schools parade in the Sambadrome, a special stadium in the centre of the city. The stadium is only used for carnival and a group of judges choose the best parade. The competition is very important, so I had to learn how to do the dance, including all the correct facial expressions and gestures.

When I arrived at the samba school, the first thing they did was fit my costume. The theme of the parade this year was the history of Brazil and the costume was designed to look like the sabiá-laranjeira, a bird which is one of the national symbols of Brazil. For the next two days, I practised the dance with the rest of the samba school. ⁴_____

Finally, on Saturday night, it was time for our parade. We arrived at the Sambadrome at midnight, but we weren't on until 3 a.m. ⁵_____ The place was amazing. There were thousands of spectators, and you could hear them cheering above the noise of the drums and singing. As we walked out, I felt happier than I'd ever felt before in my life.

On Wednesday, the winner was announced. It wasn't our school, but we came third. I was really happy with that. It was altogether an unforgettable experience.

a On the way, we passed lots of impressive sights, including the famous Copacabana beach.
b None of us were tired, though, because we were all so nervous!
c Things really started to get going on Monday.
d It took a long time to get to the Sambadrome because of that.
e This year, over two million people took part!
f It was hard work, especially because the temperature was over thirty-five degrees!
g However, the atmosphere in the city is very exciting for days before that.
h What none of us realised was that the music went on all night!

6 Read the advert and answer the questions.

Exam tip: Highlight the key words in each question so you know what type of information to look for in the text.

1 How long is the course? _twelve weeks_
2 Apart from people who are already working, who is the course for? _____
3 What type of techniques will you learn?
   _____
4 What can you do if you miss a lesson?
   _____
5 What do you get when you finish the course?
   _____

GOVEL COLLEGE
Short online course in illustration

Our illustration course lasts twelve weeks and is fully online. It is perfect for beginners or people who want to add to their skills portfolio, such as interior designers, illustrators for children's books or people who design logos for clothes. The course aims to:
- help you develop your personal style.
- teach a range of drawing techniques.
- help you create your own portfolio.
- show how you can use your designs to communicate emotions.

The course includes:
- recorded online lessons (in case you can't attend it)
- a basic software package.
- a certificate when you successfully complete the course.

Exam Time 3 — Reading and Writing — Units 1–9

7 Read the text and answer the questions.

1. What is Banner Repeater?
   an art gallery
2. Who displays their exhibitions and performances there? _____
3. Where does the name of the art gallery come from? _____
4. Where does the money for it come from today? _____
5. What can you do if you want to? _____

Platform art

Banner Repeater is an art gallery on platform 1 of Hackney Downs train station in London, where you can see exhibitions and performances by local artists. It is named after a type of train signal. More specifically the name refers to the function of the signal, which is to repeat an earlier signal on the track, in case the driver isn't able to see it the first time.

The gallery was originally paid for by an 'Art in Empty Spaces' project. Nowadays, it is supported by Hackney Council, with money for projects which develop empty urban spaces. The artists whose work appears in the gallery publish posters which you don't have to pay for, though you are welcome to make a donation.

8 Read the text and complete the sentences. Use 1–3 words from the text in each gap.

> **Exam tip**
> Change the gapped sentences into questions to help you find the right information.

1. Amanda Gorman is from *Los Angeles*.
2. She has got _____ sisters.
3. She didn't _____ when she was young.
4. She first found out about poetry from _____.
5. She found it difficult to _____.
6. Her organisation helps young writers improve _____.
7. In 2021, she read one of her poems at a _____.

AMANDA GORMAN

Amanda Gorman is an American poet and activist. She was born in Los Angeles on 7 March 1998 and grew up with her two sisters, including her twin Gabrielle. The family was raised by their single mother, Joan Wicks, an English teacher. The children didn't watch much TV when they were growing up, and Amanda liked to read and write, which her mother encouraged. She also enjoyed writing stories. Then one day at school, her teacher introduced her to poetry, which she loved. Amanda went on to win a scholarship to study sociology at Harvard, a well-known university in the USA.

Amanda had a speech impediment when she was growing up, which made it difficult for her to say certain words. However, she believes this really helped her perform as a poet because she had to work hard to overcome her speech impediment when performing her poems.

She has also worked hard for others, campaigning on issues related to race and feminism. In 2016, she started an organisation called One Pen One Page, which works to help children develop their writing skills.

As a poet, she has been very successful and in April 2017 she was the first person ever to become National Youth Poet Laureate of the USA. The high point came in January 2021, when she performed her poem The Hill We Climb at the inauguration ceremony of President Joe Biden. Shortly after this, two of her published books became bestsellers.

Nowadays she continues to write and perform. She also continues her social justice work, which she strongly believes can make the world a better place.

9 Write an opinion essay answering the question below. Write around 100 words and include the following information.

- an introduction
- the advantages of social media
- the disadvantages of social media
- a conclusion

> **Is social media a good thing for teenagers?**

Self-checks answer key

Unit 1 Self-check

Exercise 1
1 surprised   2 anxious   3 make
4 curious   5 generous   6 succeed
7 go   8 done

Exercise 2
1 up   2 out   3 off   4 on   5 with   6 down

Exercise 3
1 population   2 immigrants   3 support
4 explore   5 face   6 miss

Exercise 4
1 are/'re staying   2 gets up   3 am/'m having
4 is not/isn't enjoying   5 Does your mum like

Exercise 5
1 have not/haven't been   2 decided
3 have/'ve ever had   4 was   5 saw
6 talked   7 was not/wasn't
8 were walking   9 were waiting   10 met

Exercise 6
1 mind   2 get   3 give   4 minute   5 can

Unit 2 Self-check

Exercise 1
1 factory   2 waste   3 pollute   4 damaged
5 recycling centre   6 atmosphere

Exercise 2
1 away   2 animals   3 climate   4 carbon
5 waste   6 energy

Exercise 3
1 electric   2 bags   3 sources   4 centre
5 up   6 reduce   7 sign   8 hold

Exercise 4
1 had/'d got up   2 had organised
3 had/'d agreed   4 had/'d been
5 had done   6 had/'d dropped
7 had/'d collected

Exercise 5
1 won
2 did not/didn't use to care
3 used to recycle
4 Did Jo help
5 didn't/did not use to have
6 Did Luke use to be
7 did not/didn't learn
8 Did you use to leave the lights on?

Exercise 6
1 totally   2 say   3 agree   4 not   5 think

Unit 3 Self-check

Exercise 1
1 pocket   2 flowery   3 pads   4 button
5 freckles   6 sandals   7 mask   8 twenties
9 sleeves   10 heels

Exercise 2
1 d   2 f   3 a   4 e   5 c   6 i   7 h   8 b
9 g   10 j

Exercise 3
1 have/'ve been working
2 has/'s been studying
3 all   4 have not/haven't been waiting
5 for   6 since   7 all

Exercise 4
1 have/'ve been tidying
2 have/'ve found / have/'ve been finding
3 have/'ve had
4 have/'ve grown
5 have/'ve been thinking / have/'ve thought
6 have/'ve found
7 have/'ve been doing
8 have not/haven't finished

Exercise 5
1 think   2 of   3 suit   4 day   5 look

Unit 4 Self-check

Exercise 1
1 psychologist   2 cleaner   3 travel agent
4 mechanic   5 fashion designer
6 influencer   7 film director   8 interpreter

Exercise 2
1 flexible working hours   2 salary
3 well-paid   4 pay rise
5 temporary contract   6 member of staff

Exercise 3
1 career   2 blogger   3 employer
4 holidays   5 awards   6 interview

Exercise 4
1 am/'m going to watch
2 will/'ll make   3 will pass   4 leaves
5 is/'s going to rain
6 are you going to do/are you doing
7 stops   8 am/'m staying/am going to stay

Exercise 5
1 will/'ll be living   2 will/'ll be working
3 will not/won't be doing   4 will/'ll be moving
5 will/'ll be going   6 will/'ll be applying
7 will/'ll be studying

Exercise 6
1 out   2 to sit   3 to listen   4 to feed … Make

Unit 5 Self-check

Exercise 1
1 engine   2 satellite   3 galaxy   4 orbit
5 star   6 Gravity

Exercise 2
1 million   2 astronomer   3 comet
4 solar system   5 width   6 telescope
7 height   8 planet

Exercise 3
1 from   2 long   3 an   4 and   5 eight   6 high

Exercise 4
1 had   2 go   3 have met   4 won't come
5 were   6 wins   7 had left   8 travel

Exercise 5
1 will/'ll achieve   2 study   3 won
4 would/'d travel   5 will not/won't be
6 play   7 would you do

Exercise 6
1 a   2 b   3 c   4 a   5 c

Unit 6 Self-check

Exercise 1
1 blood test   2 injury   3 muscles
4 bones   5 virus   6 bite   7 symptoms
8 plasters   9 medicine   10 spray

Exercise 2
1 running   2 parachuting   3 rafting
4 sandboarding   5 paddleboarding

Exercise 3
1 operation   2 painful   3 treatment
4 illness   5 allergic

Exercise 4
1 had   2 was   3 was   4 that
5 would   6 was   7 did   8 would
9 him   10 did

Exercise 5
1 The doctor told me to stay in bed and get some rest.
2 I asked my friend to help me change my bandage.
3 The nurse told him to take the medicine twice a day.
4 Sally asked us to be quiet.
5 Kevin's mum told him not to touch that.

Exercise 6
1 any … you   2 should … help … good

Unit 7 Self-check

Exercise 1
1 billboard   2 eye   3 follow   4 leaflet
5 commercials   6 voice

Exercise 2
1 pronunciation   2 definition   3 information
4 description   5 discussion   6 suggestion
7 communication   8 explanation

Exercise 3
1 c   2 b   3 e   4 a   5 f   6 d

Exercise 4
1 were given lots of homework by our Maths teacher
2 is played in Brazil
3 has been advertised on billboards
4 must be followed at all times
5 cannot/can't be taken in here
6 has been announced by Flyby
7 was told it was OK
8 has been created

Exercise 5
1 will be opened   2 will be offered
3 will be taught   4 will be included
5 will be built   6 will be located
7 will be improved

Exercise 6
1 When … say   2 Are … what … say

Unit 8 Self-check

Exercise 1
1 photography   2 portrait   3 app
4 author   5 designer   6 weather forecast
7 headlines   8 plot

Exercise 2
1 cover   2 biography   3 non-fiction
4 author   5 novel   6 chapter

Exercise 3
1 perform   2 create   3 published
4 design   5 visit   6 has

Exercise 4
1 was not/wasn't able to call
2 Will you be able to return
3 could not/couldn't swim
4 Did you manage to finish
5 will not/won't be able to go

Exercise 5
1 have to … have to   2 Were … had
3 to leave … won't   4 Is … is allowed to
5 must … don't have to

Exercise 6
1 On   2 other   3 In   4 see   5 concerned

Unit 9 Self-check

Exercise 1
1 prom   2 ceremony   3 festival   4 get-together
5 threw   6 prepared   7 dinner   8 put
9 turn   10 stay

Exercise 2
1 special   2 reception   3 costume   4 carnival
5 surprise   6 unwrap   7 celebrate
8 together   9 light   10 parade

Exercise 3
1 whose   2 which   3 who   4 where
5 where   6 whose   7 who   8 whose

Exercise 4
1 what time the parade starts
2 where I can/could catch a bus
3 if Mark went to the party   4 how old you are
5 if they have/'ve sold many tickets
6 where the concert will be   7 what it means

Exercise 5
1 Sorry   2 mind   3 ahead   4 pass   5 Here

Pearson Education Limited
KAO Two
KAO Park
Hockham Way
Harlow, Essex
CM17 9SR
England
and Associated Companies throughout the world.

pearsonenglish.com/widerworld2e

© Pearson Education Limited 2022

All rights reserved; no part of this publication may be reproduced, stored in a retrieval system, or transmitted in any form or by any means, electronic, mechanical, photocopying, recording, or otherwise without the prior written permission of the Publishers.

First published 2022

ISBN: 978-1-292-42280-0

Set in Frutiger Next Pro
Printed in Mexico

Acknowledgements

The Publishers would like to thank all the teachers and students around the world who contributed to the development of Wider World Second Edition: Milena Aleksić, Tuğba Arslantaş, Gülşah Aslan, Mahgol Baboorian, Katarzyna Beliniak, Burcu Candan, Seri Diri, Hanna Dudich, Sema Karapinar, Nadiia Kasianchuk, Duygu Kayhan, Iryna Kharchenko, Ana Krstić, Ilknur Manav, Fulya Mertoğlu, Ivana Nikolov, Banu Oflas, Duygu Özer, Jagoda Popović, Marija Šanjević, Karmen Irizar Segurola, Elif Sevinç, Ludmila Shengel, Ayşe Sönmez, Anna Standish, Natalia Tkachenko, Pamela Van Bers, Jelena Vračar, Agnieszka Woźnicka, Münevver Yanık.

The Publishers would like to thank the following people who commented on the Wider World Second Edition content: Milena Aleksić, Mahgol Baboorian, Hanna Dudich, Izabela Kołando, Karmen Irizar Segurola, Joanna Srokosz, Anna Zając.

We would also like to thank the authors of the first edition of Wider World whose work has been the basis for creating this adaptation: Kathryn Alevizos, Carolyn Barraclough, Catherine Bright, Sheila Dignen, Lynda Edwards, Rod Fricker, Suzanne Gaynor, Bob Hastings, Jennifer Heath, Liz Kilbey, Stuart McKinlay, Sarah Thorpe, Tasia Vassilatou, Damian Williams, Sandy Zervas.

Photo Acknowledgements

123RF.com: Alberto Gonzalez 96, alinamd 26, archangel80880 48, arturaliev 26, chic2view 26, Claudio Ventrella 48, delcreations 83, dolgachov 59, federicofoto 4, Franck Boston 80, gstockstudio 38, Hongqi Zhang 90, Ian Allenden 38, imagesource 4, ivanzkart 49, jirkaejc 65, Jozef Polc 90, Korarkar 48, olegdudko 13, paulphoto 22, Sergiy Tryapitsyn 32, Stanislav Sablin 7, vilainecrevette 4;
Getty Images: adamkaz 41, AMR Image 61, bjones27 38, Cavan Images 90, Cicy 38, Colorblind Images LLC 38, filadendron 41, Gary Yeowell 80, Image Source 21, Imgorthand 90, J Galione 4, Kali9 5, LeoPatrizi 17, 19, Mads Perch 11, Morsa Images 80, Pollyana Ventura 95, recep-bg 71, Rob Carr 110, SDI Productions 58, SerrNovik 97, sinology 38, Susan Wood 36, Thatphichai Yodsri/EyeEm 16, Tolimir 44, wundervisuals 91; **Pearson Education Ltd:** 68, 100, Gareth Boden 103, 103, Miguel Dominguez Munoz 103, Pearson Education Asia Ltd/Coleman Yuen 4, Sophie Bluy 93; **Shutterstock:** Alex Mit 48, Altrendo Images 109, Andrey_Popov 38, Asier Romero 93, Avatar_023 106, BearFotos 81, chainarong06 43, Dan Breckwoldt 104, DanieleGay 51, Elena Schweitzer 59, Everett - Art 80, Ferveez Mohideen 90, George Rudy 38, Gorodenkoff 80, hedgehog111 41, insta_photos 85, Karkas 26, Kenny Tong 4, Kirill Demchenko 26, lassedesignen 77, MarcelClemens 48, Matt Gibson 87, 87, Micha Rosenwirth 48, michaeljung 93, Michal Durinik 80, Mircea Bezergheanu 80, Molodec 105, muratart 48, Nasky 48, Operation Shooting 90, OSORIOartist 53, photosounds 26, Pressmaster 103, Tragoolchitr Jittasaiyapan 48, Tyler Olson 38, Vadim Sadovski 48, ZouZou 103

Illustrated by Laura Arias (Beehive Illustration) 3,31,49,75; Tim Bradford (IllustrationX) 21,63,127,130,134; David Cuzik 100; Gergely Fórizs (Beehive Illustration) 101; Julián Totino 68; Rupert Van Wyk (Beehive Illustration) 6,27,70

All other images © Pearson Education

Cover photo © Front: **Getty Images:** Copyrights by Sigfrid López